Algebra II

7
DAY
BOOK

D1312705

Assignments

TXT
512
C2155
v.2
pt.2

 **Carnegie Learning**®
THE COGNITIVE TUTOR® COMPANY

THE COGNITIVE TUTOR® COMPANY

Pittsburgh, PA
Phone 888.851.7094
Fax 412.690.2444

www.carnegielearning.com

Acknowledgements

We would like to thank those listed below who helped to prepare the Cognitive Tutor®
Algebra II Assignments.

William S. Hadley
The Carnegie Learning Development Team

Mathematics was used in a variety of ways to create the building on the front cover.
Architects designed the front of the building with curves that were structurally sound and
pleasing to the eye. Interior designers created windows and rooms which optimized the use
of ambient light while minimizing heating and cooling costs. As you work through the
Cognitive Tutor® *Algebra II* text and software, you will see additional opportunities for using
mathematics in you everyday activities.

ISBN 978-1-934800-18-8
Assignments

Printed in the United States of America
1-7/2008-HPS
2-4/2009 HPS

Assignment

Name _____   Date _____

Tanks a Lot
Introduction to Linear Functions

You decide to mow lawns during the summer to make money. You spend $340 to purchase equipment such as a lawn mower, rakes, and garbage cans. You decide to charge $20 per lawn.

1. In this problem, what are the two quantities that are changing?

2. Which quantity is the independent quantity? Which quantity is the dependent quantity?

3. Let the variable x represent the independent quantity and let the variable y represent the dependent quantity. Write an equation that shows the relationship between the two quantities.

4. Use your equation to calculate your profit if you mow 12 lawns.

5. Use your equation to calculate your profit if you mow 20 lawns.

6. How many lawns have you mowed if your profit is $160?

7. How many lawns have you mowed if your profit is $420?

8. Use your answers to Questions 1–7 to complete the table.

Quantity Name		
Unit		
Expression		

9. Use the table to construct a graph that represents the problem situation.

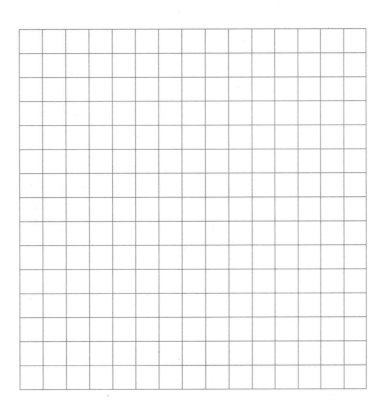

10. Use your graph to determine the number of lawns that you have to mow if you want to make a profit of $540.

Assignment

Name _____ Date _____

Calculating Answers
Solving Linear Equations and Linear Inequalities in One Variable

Solve each equation.

1. $x - 8 = 15$

2. $-9 = 4 + y$

3. $\dfrac{c}{-1.2} = 5$

4. $2x + 5 = 1$

5. $0.4w - 3 = -2$

6. $\dfrac{t}{2} + 1 = 15$

Solve each inequality and graph the solution on a number line.

7. $5x - 6 \leq 29$

8. $-8 \neq \dfrac{h}{3} + 7$

9. $-3(2d + 4) < 18$

10. An artist is selling her paintings at an art show for $30 each. She wants to make at least $200. Write an inequality to represent the problem situation, where *x* represents the number of paintings the artist sells. Then determine the number of paintings she needs to sell to meet her goal.

Name _____ Date _____

Running a 10K
Slope-Intercept Form of Linear Functions

Identify the slope and *y*-intercept of the linear function.

1. $y = 3x + 5$

2. $y = -\frac{1}{2}x - 4$

3. $y = 0.8x - 1.5$

4. $y = -6x$

Determine the slope and *y*-intercept of the linear function that passes through the given points.

5. (0, 1) and (6, 4)

6. (−2, 0) and (0, −8)

7. (−1, −8) and (3, 0)

8. (5, −1) and (−10, 8)

A machine in a canning factory manufactures 50 tin cans every hour. Currently, 200 tin cans have been manufactured.

9. What are the two quantities that are changing? Identify the independent quantity and the dependent quantity.

10. Identify the slope and *y*-intercept. What do these values mean in the context of the problem?

11. Let the variable *x* represent the independent quantity, and let the variable *y* represent the dependent quantity. Write an equation in slope-intercept form that shows the relationship between the two quantities.

12. Graph the linear function that represents the problem situation using the slope and *y*-intercept.

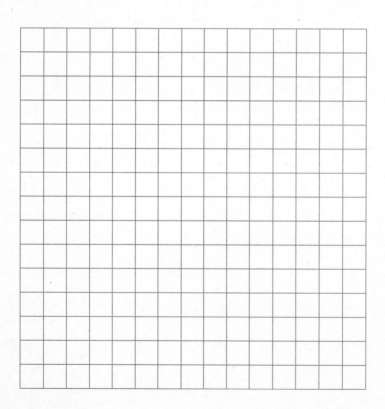

Assignment

Name _____ Date _____

1

Pump It Up
Standard Form of Linear Functions

Rewrite each linear equation in standard form. Then determine the *x*- and *y*-intercepts.

1. $y = 6x - 12$

2. $y = -4x + 1$

3. $y = \dfrac{3}{4}x + 5$

4. $y = -0.5x - 2$

Rewrite each linear equation in slope-intercept form. Then determine the slope and *y*-intercept.

5. $2x - y = -7$

6. $5x + y = 2$

7. $-3x + 4y = -4$　　　　　　　　**8.** $5x + 3y = -12$

Dora is opening a coffee and tea shop. She wants to offer two types of loose leaf tea in her store—green tea and black tea. A local supplier sells green tea for $25 per pound and black tea for $16 per pound. Dora has a budget of $200 to spend on the tea.

9. Let the variable x represent the number of pounds of green tea that Dora buys. Let the variable y represent the number of pounds of black tea that Dora buys. Write an equation in standard form to represent the total amount that Dora spends on tea.

10. If Dora buys 4 pounds of green tea, how many pounds of black tea can she buy?

11. If Dora buys 7.5 pounds of black tea, how many pounds of green tea can she buy?

12. Determine the x- and y-intercepts. What do the x- and y-intercepts represent in the context of the problem?

13. Use the intercepts to graph the linear function that represents the problem situation.

Assignment

Name _____ Date _____

Shifts and Flips
Basic Functions and Linear Transformations

Graph the basic function $y = x$ on each grid. Then graph the given function and describe the transformation that was performed on the basic function to result in the given function. Describe the transformation both algebraically and graphically.

1. $y = x - 5$

2. $y = 3x$

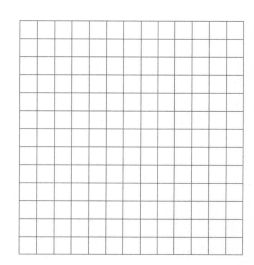

3. $y = \dfrac{1}{2}x + 4$

4. $y = -2x - 3$

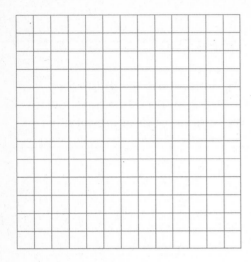

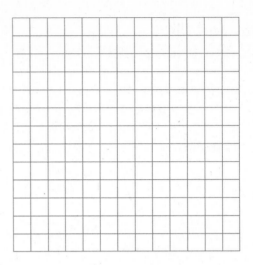

Graph the basic function $y = x$ on each grid. Then graph the function that results after performing the given transformation on the parent function. Then write an equation for the new function.

1. Shift up 2 units.

2. Reflect in the x-axis.

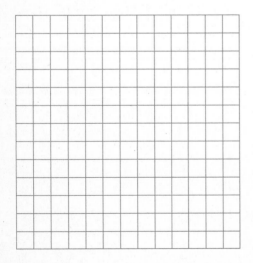

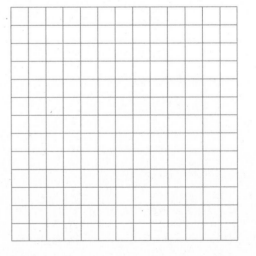

3. Dilate by 4. Then shift down 3 units.

4. Dilate by $\frac{1}{3}$. Then reflect in *x*-axis.

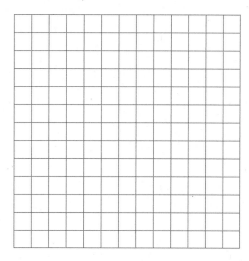

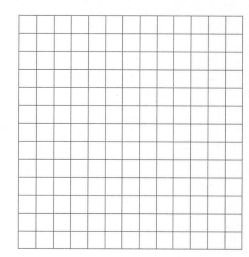

Assignment

Name _____ Date _____

Inventory and Sand
Determining the Equations of Linear Functions

Write the equation of the line in slope-intercept form using the given information.

1. The slope of the line is 3 and the y-intercept is -10.

2. The slope of the line is $-\dfrac{5}{3}$ and a point on the line is $(3, -1)$.

3. Two points on the line are $(-2, 1)$ and $(6, 33)$.

4. A point on the line is (5, −4) and the equation of a line parallel to the line is
   $y = 0.2x + 1$.

5. A point on the line is (−6, −1) and the equation of a line perpendicular to the line is
   $y = 2x − 7$.

You plant a small seedling. After 2 weeks, the plant is 154 millimeters tall. After 5 weeks, the plant is 226 millimeters tall. Assume that the plant grows at a constant rate.

6. What are the two quantities that are changing? Identify the independent quantity and the dependent quantity.

7. Identify the two points given in the problem statement.

8. Determine the slope of the line that represents the problem situation. What does the slope mean in the context of the problem?

9. Let the variable x represent the independent quantity and let the variable y represent the dependent quantity. Write an equation in slope-intercept form that shows the relationship between the two quantities.

10. What was the height of the seedling when you first planted it?

11. How long will it take the plant to reach a height of 1 meter, if it continues to grow at the same rate?

Assignment

Name _____ Date _____

Absolutely!
Absolute Value Equations and Inequalities

Solve each equation.

1. $|x + 9| = 6.$

2. $|4x - 2| = -1$

3. $|0.8x - 3| = 10$

4. $50 = |16x + 30|$

Graph the solutions to each equation.

5. $y = |x - 1|$

6. $y = \left|\dfrac{4}{3}x + 2\right|$

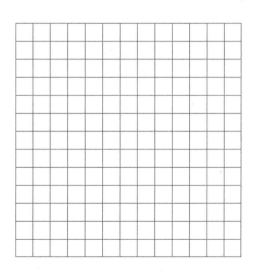

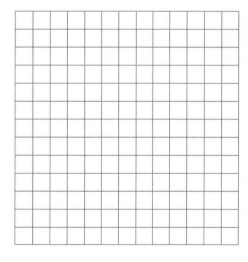

Solve each inequality and plot the solutions on the number line.

7. $|5 - x| < 8$

8. $|6x + 7| \geq 4$

$\longleftrightarrow\!\!\!+\!\!\!+\!\!\!+\!\!\!+\!\!\!+\!\!\!+\!\!\!+\!\!\!+\!\!\!+\!\!\!+\!\!\!+\!\!\!\longrightarrow$ $\qquad\longleftrightarrow\!\!\!+\!\!\!+\!\!\!+\!\!\!+\!\!\!+\!\!\!+\!\!\!+\!\!\!+\!\!\!+\!\!\!+\!\!\!+\!\!\!\longrightarrow$

9. $|2.4x - 3| \leq 9$

10. $|11 - 5x| > 24$

$\longleftrightarrow\!\!\!+\!\!\!+\!\!\!+\!\!\!+\!\!\!+\!\!\!+\!\!\!+\!\!\!+\!\!\!+\!\!\!+\!\!\!+\!\!\!\longrightarrow$ $\qquad\longleftrightarrow\!\!\!+\!\!\!+\!\!\!+\!\!\!+\!\!\!+\!\!\!+\!\!\!+\!\!\!+\!\!\!+\!\!\!+\!\!\!+\!\!\!\longrightarrow$

Graph the solutions to each inequality.

11. $y \geq |x + 4|$

12. $y < |3x - 9|$

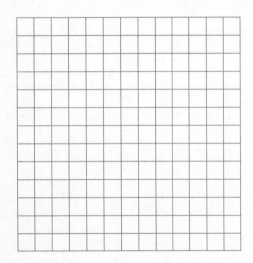
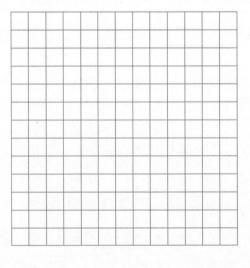

Assignment

Name _____ Date _____

Inverses and Pieces
Functional Notation, Inverses, and Piecewise Functions

Write each linear equation using functional notation, then determine the inverse of the function. Check your answers.

1. $y = x - 12$

2. $y - 3x = 0$

3. $2y = 4x + 2$

4. $7 = 0.4x - y$

5. $2x - 3y = -15$ **6.** $-6x = 10 - y$

You are running for class president. You would like to purchase campaign buttons to pass out to the students in your school. A company that designs and prints the buttons charges a flat fee of $5 plus $0.75 per button for the first 50 buttons you purchase. They charge $0.40 per button for the next 50 buttons you purchase and $0.25 for each button purchased after the first 100 buttons.

7. Let x represent the number of buttons that you purchase. Write a piecewise function to represent the total cost if you buy x buttons.

8. Calculate the total cost for purchasing each number of buttons below.

   a. 25 buttons

   b. 50 buttons

   c. 75 buttons

d. 100 buttons

e. 150 buttons

f. 300 buttons

9. Use your answers to Question 8 to complete the table of values below. Then graph the function.

Number of buttons purchased	Total cost (dollars)
25	
50	
75	
100	
150	
300	

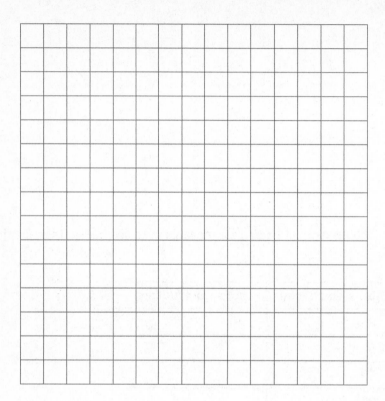

10. Use the graph to estimate the number of buttons you could purchase for $100.

11. Suppose that another company charges a flat printing fee of $5 plus $0.50 per button for any number of buttons purchased. When would it make sense to choose this company over the other?

Assignment

Name _____ Date _____

Finding a Job
Introduction to Systems of Linear Equations

You would like to take a taxicab to the airport. There are two local taxicab companies. Friendly's Cab Company charges $2.60 upon entry and an additional $0.20 per one-sixth mile driven. Anderson Taxi, Inc., charges $5.00 upon entry and an additional $0.10 per one-sixth mile driven.

1. For Friendly's Cab Company, what are the two quantities that are changing? Identify which quantity is the independent quantity and which quantity is the dependent quantity.

2. Let the variable x represent the independent quantity and let the variable y represent the dependent quantity. Write an equation that shows the relationship between the two quantities for Friendly's Cab Company.

3. For Anderson Taxi, Inc., what are the two quantities that are changing? Identify which quantity is the independent quantity and which quantity is the dependent quantity.

4. Let the variable x represent the independent quantity and let the variable y represent the dependent quantity. Write an equation that shows the relationship between the two quantities for Anderson Taxi, Inc.

5. Suppose that the airport is 3 miles away. Determine the cost of using Friendly's Cab Company, and then determine the cost of using Anderson Taxi, Inc. Which cab company would you use? Explain your reasoning.

6. Suppose that the airport is 5 miles away. Determine the cost of using Friendly's Cab Company and then determine the cost of using Anderson Taxi, Inc. Which cab company would you use? Explain your reasoning.

7. Graph both of the functions on the grid.

8. Determine the point of intersection of the graphs of the functions. What does the point of intersection mean in the context of the problem? How does this help you decide which taxicab company to use?

2

Assignment

Name _____ Date _____

Pens-R-Us
Solving Systems of Linear Equations: Graphing and Substitution

A health food company has decided to produce a new line of energy bars. The start-up costs to produce the new line of energy bars are $8280. It costs the company $0.062 to make each energy bar. The health food company sells the energy bars to stores in boxes of 50 for $17.50 per box.

1. What are the two quantities that are changing for the cost of the new line of energy bars? Identify which quantity is the independent quantity and which quantity is the dependent quantity.

2. Let the variable x represent the independent quantity and let the variable y represent the dependent quantity. Write an equation that shows the relationship between the two quantities for the cost of producing the new line of energy bars.

3. How much would it cost for the company to produce 1000 energy bars? 10,000 energy bars? 50,000 energy bars?

4. How many energy bars can the company produce if it spends $20,000?

5. What are the two quantities that are changing for selling the new line of energy bars? Identify which quantity is the independent quantity and which quantity is the dependent quantity.

6. Let the variable x represent the independent quantity and let the variable y represent the dependent quantity. Write an equation that shows the relationship between the two quantities for the cost of producing the new line of energy bars.

7. How much would the company receive if it sold 1000 energy bars? 10,000 energy bars? 50,000 energy bars?

8. If the company has a goal to make $20,000 in sales of energy bars, how many energy bars does it need to sell?

9. Graph both of the functions on the grid.

10. Use the substitution method to determine the point of intersection of the two lines.

11. What does the point of intersection represent in this problem situation?

Use the method of substitution to determine the point of intersection for each system of linear equations.

12. $\begin{cases} y = -2x + 4 \\ x = y + 5 \end{cases}$

13. $\begin{cases} 2x + 3y = 14 \\ y = 5x - 1 \end{cases}$

14. $\begin{cases} y = -4x + 9 \\ 6x + y = 10 \end{cases}$

15. $\begin{cases} 2x - 0.8y = 0 \\ -2.5x + 0.2y = 4 \end{cases}$

Assignment

Name _____ Date _____

Tickets
Solving Systems of Linear Equations: Linear Combinations

An investor owns shares of stock in two companies. After the first month, the stock in the first company was worth $5.28 per share and the stock in the second company was worth $4.50 per share, for a total of $188.56. After the second month, the stock in the first company was worth $3.33 per share and the stock in the second company was worth $9.00 per share, for a total of $242.16.

1. Define variables for the quantities that are changing. Then write an equation for the total amount the investor's stocks were worth after the first month.

2. Use the variables to write an equation for the total amount the investor's stocks were worth after the second month.

3. Determine the x- and y-intercepts of the equation for the total amount the stocks were worth after the first month.

4. Determine the x- and y-intercepts of the equation for the total amount the stocks were worth after the second month.

5. Use the *x*- and *y*-intercepts to graph both equations.

6. What does the point of intersection represent in the problem situation?

7. Use the linear combination method to determine the point of intersection.

Name_____ Date _____

Use the method of linear combinations to solve each system of linear equations.

8. $\begin{cases} 3x + 4y = 14 \\ 5x - 8y = -50 \end{cases}$

9. $\begin{cases} 48x + 56y = 380 \\ 16x + 30y = 87 \end{cases}$

10. $\begin{cases} 2.8x - 5.7y = -13.95 \\ 1.4x + 2y = -9.4 \end{cases}$

11. $\begin{cases} \dfrac{1}{2}x - \dfrac{5}{6}y = -\dfrac{31}{4} \\ \dfrac{2}{3}x - 2y = -21 \end{cases}$

Assignment

Name _____ Date _____

Cramer's Rule
Solving Systems of Linear Equations: Cramer's Rule

Calculate the determinant of each array.

1. $\begin{vmatrix} 2 & 6 \\ 5 & -1 \end{vmatrix}$

2. $\begin{vmatrix} -36 & -15 \\ 49 & 0 \end{vmatrix}$

3. $\begin{vmatrix} -6.2 & 3.1 \\ 1.6 & -0.8 \end{vmatrix}$

4. $\begin{vmatrix} -\dfrac{2}{3} & \dfrac{5}{4} \\ -\dfrac{8}{15} & -\dfrac{9}{2} \end{vmatrix}$

Use Cramer's Rule to solve each system of linear equations.

5. $\begin{cases} 2x + 7y = 10 \\ -3x - 5y = 7 \end{cases}$

6. $\begin{cases} 3x - 6y = 6 \\ 5x - 8y = 8 \end{cases}$

7. $\begin{cases} 1.4x + 4y = 5.5 \\ 3.2x + 4.5y = 7 \end{cases}$

8. $\begin{cases} \dfrac{3}{4}x - \dfrac{1}{3}y = -\dfrac{1}{6} \\ -9x + 8y = -2 \end{cases}$

Use any method (graphing, substitution, linear combinations, or Cramer's Rule) to solve each system of linear equations.

9. $\begin{cases} y = 2x + 5 \\ y = -7x - 4 \end{cases}$

10. $\begin{cases} y = 6x - 2 \\ x = -0.5y + 2 \end{cases}$

11. $\begin{cases} 4x + 11y = -23 \\ -3x - 15y = 51 \end{cases}$

12. $\begin{cases} 4x - 12y = -36 \\ 9x + 3y = -91 \end{cases}$

2

Assignment

Name _____ Date _____

Consistent and Independent
Systems of Linear Equations: Consistent and Independent

Answer the following questions about systems of linear equations.

1. How many solutions does a system of linear equations have if it is consistent?

2. How many solutions does a system of linear equations have if it is inconsistent?

3. How many solutions does a system of linear equations have if it is linearly independent?

4. How many solutions does a system of linear equations have if it is linearly dependent?

Solve each system of linear equations. Then determine whether the system is consistent or inconsistent and whether it is dependent or independent.

5. $\begin{cases} 2x + 5y = 0 \\ -6x - 9y = 24 \end{cases}$

6. $\begin{cases} -0.4x + 3y = -3.3 \\ 1.5x + 2y = 19 \end{cases}$

7. $\begin{cases} y = 4x + 6 \\ 12x - 3y = -18 \end{cases}$

8. $\begin{cases} 9x + 4y = 16 \\ 4.5x + 2y = 32 \end{cases}$

9. $\begin{cases} x = 18y - 150 \\ 2x - 50y = 190 \end{cases}$

10. $\begin{cases} \dfrac{2}{3}x - \dfrac{1}{4}y = 1 \\ -\dfrac{4}{5}x + 3y = 0 \end{cases}$

11. Is it possible for a system of linear equations to be both consistent and linearly independent? If so, give an example (other than a system from a previous question). If not, explain why not.

12. Is it possible for a system of linear equations to be both consistent and linearly dependent? If so, give an example (other than a system from a previous question). If not, explain why not.

13. Is it possible for a system of linear equations to be both inconsistent and linearly independent? If so, give an example (other than a system from a previous question). If not, explain why not.

14. Is it possible for a system of linear equations to be both inconsistent and linearly dependent? If so, give an example (other than a system from a previous question). If not, explain why not.

Assignment

Name _____ Date _____

Inequalities—Infinite Solutions
Solving Linear Inequalities and Systems of Linear Inequalities in Two Variables

Graph the solution set for each inequality.

1. $y \geq -4x + 9$

2. $y < \dfrac{2}{3}x - 1$

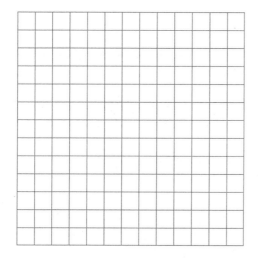
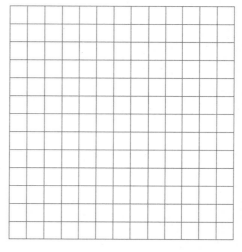

3. $3x - 5y < -2$

4. $x + 0.5y \leq -1.5$

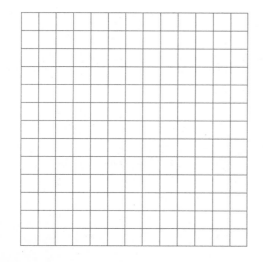
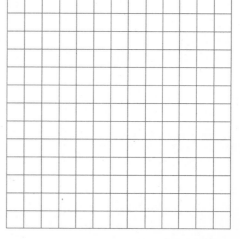

Graph the solution set for each system of inequalities.

5. $\begin{cases} y < 3x + 2 \\ y \geq -x \end{cases}$

6. $\begin{cases} y \leq -2x + 1 \\ 4x + 2y \geq -12 \end{cases}$

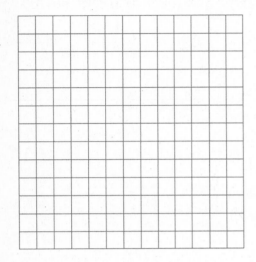

7. $\begin{cases} -3x + 3y < 3 \\ y > 2x + 1 \end{cases}$

8. $\begin{cases} y < 6 \\ x \geq -3 \end{cases}$

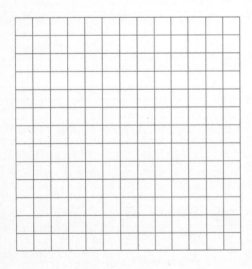

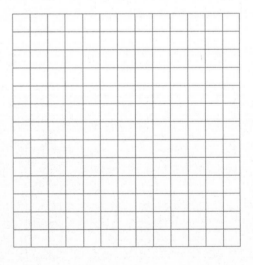

Assignment

Name _____ Date _____

Three in Three or More
Solving Systems of Three or More Linear Equations in Three or More Variables

Your school's Key Club decided to sell fruit baskets to raise money for a local charity. The club sold a total of 80 fruit baskets. There were three different types of fruit baskets. Small fruit baskets sold for $15.75 each, medium fruit baskets sold for $25 each, and large fruit baskets sold for $32.50 each. The Key Club took in a total of $2086.25, and they sold twice as many large baskets as small baskets.

1. Let the variable x represent the number of small fruit baskets sold, let y represent the number of medium fruit baskets sold, and let z represent the number of large fruit baskets sold. Write an equation that represents the total number of fruit baskets sold.

2. Use the variables from Question 1 to write an equation that represents the total amount of money the Key Club made in fruit basket sales.

3. Use the same variables to write an equation that represents the number of large fruit baskets sold compared to the number of small fruit baskets sold.

4. Use the equations in Questions 1–3 to write a system of equations in three variables.

5. Solve the system of equations in Question 4 to calculate the number of each type of fruit basket that the Key Club sold.

Solve each system by first using elimination to reduce it to a system of two equations in two variables.

6. $\begin{cases} x + 3y - 2z = 17 \\ 2x - 5y + z = -25 \\ -x - 4y - 3z = -6 \end{cases}$

7. $\begin{cases} 4x - y + z = 9.5 \\ -3x + 5y - z = -19 \\ 2x - 4y + 2z = 21 \end{cases}$

Solve each system by first using substitution to reduce it to a system of two equations in two variables.

8. $\begin{cases} 2x + 3y + z = 4 \\ 5x + 6y + 4z = 4 \\ -3x - 2y - 3z = -3 \end{cases}$

9. $\begin{cases} 5x - 3y - 8z = -99 \\ -6x + 5y + 4z = -150 \\ -10x - y + 9z = 142 \end{cases}$

Solve each system by first using Cramer's Rule to reduce it to a system of two equations in two variables.

10. $\begin{cases} 2x + 3y + 7z = -30 \\ -10x - 4y + 15z = 35 \\ 9x + 2y - 11z = -5 \end{cases}$

11. $\begin{cases} 3x + 4y - 8z = 0 \\ 5x - 4y + 2z = -9 \\ -2x + 6y - 6z = 6 \end{cases}$

Assignment

Name _____ Date _____

Lots and Rockets
Introduction to Quadratic Functions

1. The length of a rectangle is 15 inches longer than its width.

    a. Write an equation to represent the area of the rectangle.

    b. If the width of the rectangle is 18 inches, what is the area?

    c. If the length of the rectangle is 50 inches, what is the area?

Your science class launches a model rocket from the ground. The model rocket is launched upward with an initial velocity of 128 feet per second. The acceleration due to gravity is 32 feet per second squared.

2. Write an equation to model the distance the rocket travels. Let d be the distance and let t be the time in seconds.

3. How high will the rocket be after:

    a. 1 second?

    b. 3 seconds?

c. 4 seconds?

d. 6 seconds?

e. 7 seconds?

3

4. Use the information from Questions 1 and 2 to complete the table.

Quantity Name	Time	Height
Unit		
Expression	t	
	1	
	3	
	4	
	6	
	7	

5. Use the table in Question 4 to graph the height of the rocket versus the time.

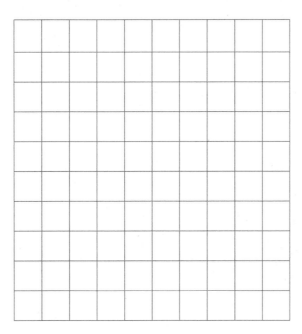

6. Use the graph to approximate the maximum height of the rocket and the amount of time it takes for the rocket to reach its maximum height.

7. Use the graph to approximate the amount of time it takes for the rocket to reach the ground.

Assignment

Name _____ Date _____

Intercepts, Vertices, and Roots
Quadratic Equations and Functions

For each quadratic function, complete the table and graph the function.
On the graph, label the *y*-intercept, *x*-intercept(s), and vertex.

1. $y = x^2 + 4x$

x	y
−5	
−3	
−2	
0	
1	

2. $y = x^2 - 2x$

x	y
−2	
−1	
1	
3	
4	

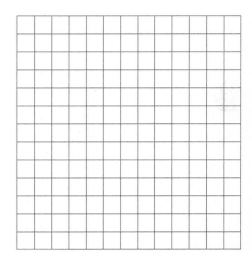

3. $y = \dfrac{1}{2}x^2$

x	y
−3	
−1	
0	
2	
4	

4. $y = -x^2 + 6x + 7$

x	y
−1	
0	
1	
4	
7	

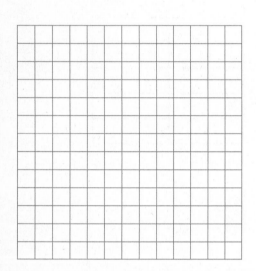

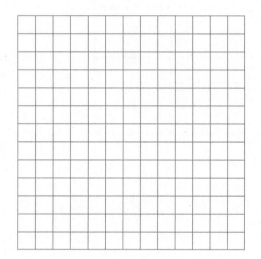

Determine the roots of each quadratic equation by factoring.

5. $x^2 + 10x = 0$

6. $12x - 4x^2 = 0$

7. $x^2 - 25 = 0$

8. $3x^2 - 27 = 0$

9. $x^2 + 4x + 4 = 0$

10. $x^2 + 6x + 5 = 0$

3

Assignment

Name _____ Date _____

Quadratic Expressions
Multiplying and Factoring

Calculate the product.

1. $x(x - 7)$

2. $3x(x + 5)$

3. $-2x(4x + 1)$

4. $0.5x(x - 0.2)$

5. $\frac{1}{2}x\left(\frac{4}{5}x + 3\right)$

6. $(x - 5)(x + 6)$

7. $(2x + 1)(x + 3)$

8. $(-2.4x - 3)(1.1x - 4.5)$

9. $\left(x + \frac{3}{4}\right)^2$

Factor the expression.

10. $x^2 + 3x - 4$

11. $x^2 + 7x + 10$

12. $x^2 - 12x + 36$

13. $x^2 - 3x - 40$

14. $5x^2 + 9x - 2$

15. $16x^2 - 1$

Determine the zero(s) for the function.

16. $y = x^2 + 8x + 12$

17. $x^2 - 13x + 30 = y$

18. $y = x^2 + 22x + 121$

19. $y = x^2 - 5x - 36$

20. $x^2 + 9x - 10 = y$

21. $x^2 - 11 = y$

22. $2x^2 - x - 1 = y$ **23.** $y = 8x^2 - 8$ **24.** $y = 3x^2 + 12x + 12$

3

Assignment

Name _____ Date _____

More Factoring
Special Products and Completing the Square

Calculate the product.

1. $(x + 7)(x - 7)$

2. $(x + 9)(x + 9)$

3. $(x - 12)(x - 12)$

4. $(x - 15)(x + 15)$

5. $(x + 6)^2$

6. $(x - 10)^2$

Factor the expression.

7. $x^2 + 2x + 1$

8. $x^2 - 16x + 64$

9. $x^2 - 9$

10. $9x^2 - 1$

11. $25x^2 - 16$

12. $4x^2 + 12x + 9$

Solve the equation by completing the square.

13. $x^2 + 6x + 2 = 0$

14. $x^2 + 10x + 5 = 0$

15. $x^2 - 8x - 3 = 0$

16. $x^2 - 20x + 40 = 0$ **17.** $x^2 + 4x - 2 = 0$ **18.** $x^2 + x - 7 = 0$

19. $x^2 - 14x + 18 = 0$ **20.** $x^2 + 3x + 1 = 0$ **21.** $x^2 - 15x - 9 = 0$

3

Assignment

Name _____ Date _____

Quadratic Formula
Solving Quadratic Equations Using the Quadratic Formula

Solve the equation by Using the Quadratic Formula.

1. $x^2 + 21x + 108 = 0$

2. $3x^2 + x - 2 = 0$

3. $x^2 - 21 = 0$

4. $x^2 - 7x - 20 = 0$

5. $3x^2 - 2x + 1 = 0$

6. $6x^2 + 5x = 0$

7. $x^2 - 2.2x + 0.85 = 0$

8. $-3x^2 - 6x - 2 = 0$

9. $4x^2 - 5x - 1 = 0$

10. $2x^2 + 10x + 11 = 0$

11. $-6x^2 - 6x + 180 = 0$

12. $3x^2 - 31x + 36 = 0$

3

Assignment

Name _____ Date _____

Graphing Quadratic Functions
Properties of Parabolas

Complete the table and graph the quadratic function. Identify the vertex, *x*-intercept(s), *y*-intercept, and axis of symmetry.

1. $y = x^2 + 4x$

x	y
−4	
−3	
−2	
−1	
0	

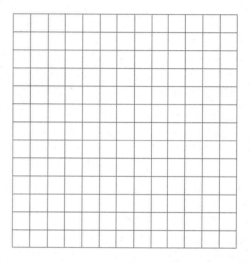

vertex: _____

x-intercept(s): _____

y-intercept: _____

axis of symmetry: _____

2. $y = x^2 − 2x − 8$

x	y
−2	
0	
1	
2	
4	

vertex: _____

x-intercept(s): _____

y-intercept: _____

axis of symmetry: _____

3. $y = -\dfrac{1}{3}x^2 + 3$

x	y
−6	
−3	
0	
3	
6	

vertex: _____

x-intercept(s): _____

y-intercept: _____

axis of symmetry: _____

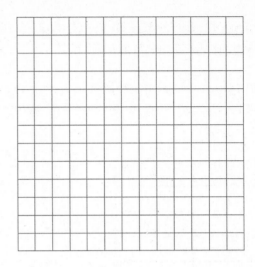

4. $y = -x^2 - 5x + 6$

x	y
−7	
−6	
−2	
0	
1	

vertex: _____

x-intercept(s): _____

y-intercept: _____

axis of symmetry: _____

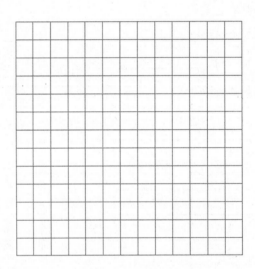

Consider the equation of a parabola $y = ax^2 + bx + c$, where a, b, and c are real numbers, and a is not equal to zero.

5. Describe the graph of $y = ax^2 + bx + c$ when a is positive.

6. Describe the graph of $y = ax^2 + bx + c$ when a is negative.

7. Describe the graph of $y = ax^2 + bx + c$ when c is positive.

8. Describe the graph of $y = ax^2 + bx + c$ when c is negative.

Assignment

Name _____ Date _____

Graphing Quadratic Functions
Basic Function and Transformations

Describe the transformation(s) of the basic function $y = x^2$ that produces the graph of each given function, where a is a positive integer.

1. $y = x^2 + a$

2. $y = x^2 - a$

3. $y = ax^2$

4. $y = -ax^2$

5. $y = \dfrac{1}{a}x^2$

6. $y = -\dfrac{1}{a}x^2$

Determine the vertex of the given function. Then graph the function and describe the transformations of the basic function $y = x^2$ that produce the graph of the given function.

7. $y = x^2 + 6x + 5$

Vertex: _____

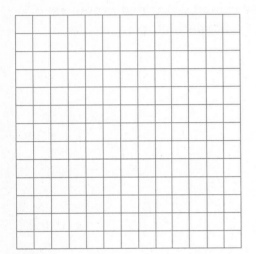

8. $y = x^2 - 8x + 15$

Vertex: _____

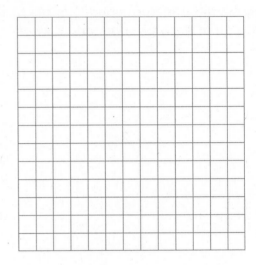

9. $y = \frac{1}{4}x^2 + 3x + 9$

Vertex: _____

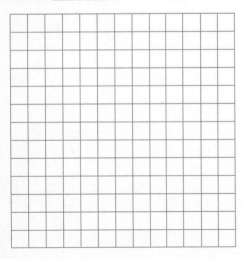

10. $y = -2x^2 - 12x - 10$

Vertex: _____

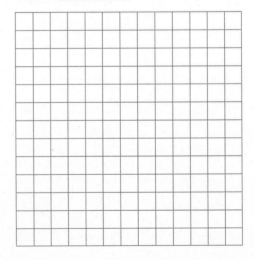

Assignment

Name _____ Date _____

Three Points Determine a Parabola
Determining Quadratic Functions

Determine the equation of the parabola that passes through the three given points.

   1. $(-1, 12)$, $(1, 2)$, $(2, 0)$

2. $(-2, 9)$, $(1, 0)$, $(2, 5)$

3. $(-4, 5)$, $(-3, 3)$, $(1, 15)$

4. (−2, 1), (−1, 2), (0, 5)

5. (6, −7), (−4, −2), (6, 0)

6. $(3, -16), (-6, -7), (-9, -16)$

Assignment

Name _____ Date _____

Time to Discriminate
The Discriminant and the Nature of Roots/Vertex Form

Use the discriminant to determine whether the function has one real root, two real roots, or no real roots. Then determine the root(s), if possible.

1. $y = 2x^2 - 2x - 24$

2. $y = 16x^2 - 24x + 9$

3. $y = 3x^2 - 246$

4. $y = x^2 + 9$

5. $y = -5x^2 - 3x + 7$

6. $y = 3x^2 + 4x + 9$

Write each function in vertex form. Then determine the vertex.

7. $y = x^2 + 10x + 15$

8. $y = 2x^2 + 4x - 6$

9. $y = -3x^2 + 12x - 7$

10. $y = 5x^2 - 40x + 79$

11. $y = -x^2 - 6x - 3$

12. $y = 4x^2 - 48x + 147$

Determine the vertex and then graph the function.

13. $y = (x + 4)^2 + 2$

Vertex: _____

14. $y = -(x + 1)^2 + 8$

Vertex: _____

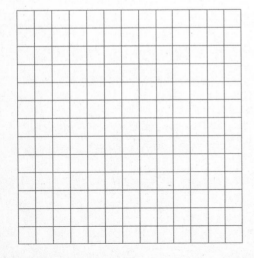

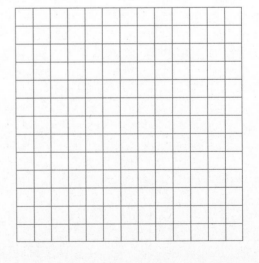

15. $y = 2(x - 3)^2 + 1$

Vertex: _____

16. $y = \frac{1}{3}(x - 6)^2 - 7$

Vertex: _____

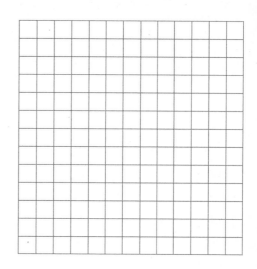

17. $y = -0.5(x - 7)^2 + 4$

Vertex: _____

18. $y = 3(x + 2)^2 - 3$

Vertex: _____

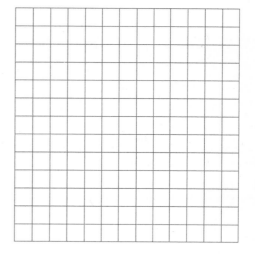

Assignment

Name _____ Date _____

Thinking About Numbers
Counting Numbers, Whole Numbers, Integers,
Rational and Irrational Numbers

Determine whether the statement is true or false. If it is false, provide a counterexample.

1. The set of natural numbers is closed under addition.

2. The set of natural numbers is closed under subtraction.

3. The set of whole numbers is closed under subtraction.

4. The set of whole numbers is closed under multiplication.

5. The set of integers is closed under subtraction.

6. The set of integers is closed under division.

7. The set of rational numbers is closed under multiplication.

8. The set of rational numbers is closed under division.

Write the repeating decimal as a fraction.

9. 0.111111...   10. 0.666666...

11. 0.8333333...

12. 0.72727272...

13. 0.41666666...

14. 0.136363636...

15. 0.2045454545...

16. 0.321321321...

Assignment

Name _____ Date _____

Real Numbers
Properties of the Real Number System

Write each symbolic statement in words. Then write the name of the property that is represented by the statement.

1. $\forall\, a, b \in \mathcal{R}, a \cdot b = b \cdot a$

2. $\forall\, a, b, c \in \mathcal{R}, (a + b) + c = a + (b + c)$

Identify the identity or property that is illustrated by each statement.

3. $2 + 1 = 1 + 2$

4. $(4 \cdot 2) \cdot 5 = 4 \cdot (2 \cdot 5)$

5. $-2(3 + 6) = (-2)(3) + (-2)(6)$

6. $\dfrac{6 - 4}{2} = \dfrac{6}{2} - \dfrac{4}{2}$

7. $10 \cdot 1 = 10$

8. $5 + 0 = 5$

9. $4 + (-4) = 0$

10. $3 \cdot \dfrac{1}{3} = 1$

Identify the property, transformation, or simplification that is used in each step to solve the equation.

11. $(3x + 9) + 5 = 2(x + 8)$

$3x + (9 + 5) = 2(x + 8)$ _____

$3x + 14 = 2(x + 8)$ _____

$3x + 14 = 2(x) + 2(8)$ _____

$3x + 14 = 2x + 16$ _____

$3x + 14 - 14 = 2x + 16 - 14$ _____

$3x + 0 = 2x + 2$ _____

$3x = 2x + 2$ _____

$3x - 2x = 2x - 2x + 2$ _____

$x = 0 + 2$ _____

$x = 2$ _____

12. $2(3x - 20) + 6 = 20$

$2(3x) - 2(20) + 6 = 20$ _____

$6x - 40 + 6 = 20$ _____

$6x - 34 = 20$ _____

$6x - 34 + 34 = 20 + 34$ _____

$6x + 0 = 54$ _____

$6x = 54$ _____

$\left(\dfrac{1}{6} \cdot 6\right) \cdot x = \dfrac{1}{6} \cdot 54$ _____

$\dfrac{1}{6} \cdot (6x) = \dfrac{1}{6} \cdot 54$ _____

$1 \cdot x = 9$ _____

$x = 9$ _____

Assignment

Name _____ Date _____

Man-Made Numbers
Imaginary Numbers and Complex Numbers

Simplify the power.

1. $4^{\frac{3}{2}}$

2. $64^{\frac{2}{3}}$

3. $(-32)^{\frac{2}{5}}$

4. $-10{,}000^{\frac{5}{4}}$

Calculate the power of i.

5. i^{10}

6. i^{88}

7. i^{105}

8. i^{0}

Calculate the square root. Simplify your answer using imaginary numbers.

9. $\sqrt{-36}$

10. $\sqrt{-49}$

11. $-\sqrt{-225}$

12. $\sqrt{-10{,}000}$

Solve the equation. Simplify your answer using imaginary numbers, if possible.

13. $x^2 + 81 = 0$

14. $2x^2 + 160 = 0$

15. $x^2 - 2x + 2 = 0$

16. $x^2 + 10x + 34 = 0$

17. $0.5x^2 - 3x + 11 = 0$

18. $-3x^2 - 2x - 9 = 0$

Assignment

Name _____ Date _____

The Complete Number System
Operations with Complex Numbers

Calculate the sum or difference.

1. $(2 + 4i) + (6 - i)$

2. $(2 - 3i) - (8 + 5i)$

3. $(-10 + 12i) - (7 - 15i)$

4. $(1 - 3.2i) + (0.5 - 4.8i)$

Calculate the product or quotient.

5. $(3 + 2i)(5 + 4i)$

6. $(9 + 6i)(9 - 6i)$

7. $\dfrac{5 - i}{1 + 2i}$

8. $\dfrac{4 - 3i}{2 - 5i}$

9. $(-7 + 2i)^2$

10. $(1 + 2i)^3$

11. $\sqrt{3 + 4i}$

12. $\sqrt{-6 + 8i}$

Assignment

Name _____ Date _____

Many Terms
Introduction to Polynomial Expressions, Equations, and Functions

Complete the table and graph the function. Then determine the (a) degree, (b) domain, (c) range, (d) x-intercept(s), and (e) y-intercept of the function.

1. $f(x) = 2x + 7$

x	y
−5	
−3	
−2	
0	
1	

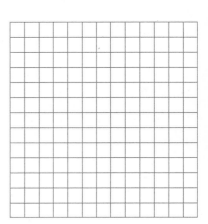

(a) Degree: _____

(b) Domain: _____

(c) Range: _____

(d) x-intercept(s): _____

(e) y-intercept: _____

2. $f(x) = 2x^4 - 20x^2 + 18$

x	y
−3	
−2	
−1	
0	
1	
2	
3	

(a) Degree: _____

(b) Domain: _____

(c) Range: _____

(d) x-intercept(s): _____

(e) y-intercept: _____

3. $f(x) = x^3 - 6x^2 + 6x + 10$

x	y
−1	
0	
2	
3	
4	
5	
6	

(a) Degree: _____

(b) Domain: _____

(c) Range: _____

(d) x-intercept(s): _____

(e) y-intercept: _____

Calculate the sum, difference, or product of the polynomials.

4. $(-5x^3 - 4x^2 + 2x - 10) + (3x^3 + 8x^2 + 7)$

5. $(2x^5 + 3x^2 - x + 3) - (x^5 + x^4 - 2x^2 + 3x)$

6. $(2x^4 + 3x^2)(4x^3 - x^2 - x)$

7. $(x^2 - 6)(x^3 + 2x^2 - x + 2)$

5

Assignment

Name _____ Date _____

Roots and Zeros
Solving Polynomial Equations and Inequalities: Factoring

Solve the equation by factoring.

1. $x^2 - 2x - 24 = 0$

2. $3x^2 = 147$

3. $x^3 + x^2 - 4x - 4 = 0$

4. $2x^3 - x^2 = 2x - 1$

5. $x^4 - 25x^2 + 144 = 0$

6. $5x^4 = 405$

Solve the inequality by factoring. Then check your answer.

7. $x^2 + 8x + 15 > 0$

8. $(x - 3)(3x + 9)(2x - 8) \geq 0$

9. $x^3 + 3x^2 - 4x - 12 < 0$

Assignment

Name _____ Date _____

Successive Approximations, Tabling, Zooming/Tracing, and Calculating
Solving Polynomial Equations: Approximations and Graphing

Use the table feature of your graphing calculator to approximate the roots of the polynomial. Approximate each root to the nearest thousandth and write your answers as ordered pairs.

1. $f(x) = x^3 + 3x^2 - 2x - 5$

2. $f(x) = 4x^3 + 9x^2 - 25x - 48$

3. $f(x) = 4x^4 - 9x^3 - 6x^2 + 18x - 4$

Use the zoom and trace features of your graphing calculator to approximate the roots of the polynomial. Approximate each root to the nearest thousandth and write your answers as ordered pairs.

4. $f(x) = x^3 + 5x^2 - 5x - 1$

5. $f(x) = x^3 - 6x^2 - 7x + 4$

6. $f(x) = 2x^3 - 11x^2 - 19x + 50$

5

Assignment

Name _____ Date _____

It's Fundamental
The Fundamental Theorem of Algebra

State the number of zeros for each polynomial function. Then, determine
the zeros by any method (factoring, successive approximation, or graphing).
State whether any zeros have a multiplicity.

1. $f(x) = x^2 - 5$

2. $f(x) = x^2 + 81$

3. $f(x) = (2x + 1)(x - 6)(x - 6)$

4. $f(x) = 5x^3 - 2x^2 - 9x$

5. $f(x) = 12x^3 + 6x^2 + 2x$

5

6. $f(x) = x^4 - 34x^2 + 225$

7. $f(x) = x^5 + 3x^4 - 9x - 27$

8. $f(x) = 3x^5 - 24x^3 + 48x$

5

Assignment

Name _____ Date _____

When Division Is Synthetic
Polynomial and Synthetic Division

Use long division to calculate the quotient of the polynomials. Write the answer as the product of the divisor and the quotient.

1. $x + 2 \overline{)4x^3 + 5x^2 - 11x - 9}$

2. $x + 1 \overline{)x^4 - 3x^3 - 2x^2 - 3x - 2}$

5

3. $x - 3 \overline{)2x^4 - 3x^3 - 19x^2 + 46x - 34}$

Use synthetic division to calculate the quotient of the polynomials. Write the answer as the product of the divisor and the quotient.

4. $x - 5 \overline{)3x^3 - 9x^2 - 31x + 5}$

5. $x + 3 \overline{)3x^4 + 13x^3 + 12x^2 + 8x + 15}$

6. $x - 4 \overline{)5x^5 - 23x^4 + 14x^3 - 18x^2 + 20x + 60}$

Assignment

Name _____ Date _____

Remains of Polynomial
The Remainder and Factor Theorems

Use the Remainder Theorem to determine the remainder of the polynomial division problem.

1. $5x^3 + 4x^2 + x + 6 \div x + 2$

2. $3x^4 - 4x^3 + 7x^2 - 2x - 4 \div x - 1$

3. $\dfrac{x^5 - 5x^4 - 2x^2 + 9}{x - 5}$

4. $\dfrac{2x^7 + 4x^6 - 5x^5 - 10x^3 - 5x^2 - 8x}{x + 3}$

Determine whether the given factor is a factor of the polynomial.

5. Polynomial: $4x^3 - 11x^2 + 11x - 10$; Factor: $x - 2$

6. Polynomial: $x^4 + 3x^3 + 3x^2 + 3x + 4$; Factor: $x + 1$

7. Polynomial: $3x^7 - 21x^6 + 4x^5 - 28x^4 - 9x^2 + 71x - 56$; Factor: $x - 7$

8. Polynomial: $x^8 + 4x^7 - 9x - 36$; Factor: $x + 4$

Use the given factor to completely factor the polynomial.

9. Polynomial: $x^3 + 3x^2 + 25x + 75$; Factor: $x + 3$

10. Polynomial: $x^4 + x^3 + 2x^2 + 8x - 48$; Factor: $x - 2$

Assignment

Assignment for Lesson 5.7

Name _____ Date _____

Out There and In-Between
Extrema and End Behavior

Use the zoom and trace features of your graphing calculator to approximate
the roots and extrema of the polynomial function.

1. $f(x) = x(x - 3)(x + 5)$

2. $f(x) = x^4 + 4x^3 - x - 4$

3. $f(x) = -(x + 2)^2(x - 1)^3$

Let *a* and *b* represent positive integers. Describe the behavior of the graph
of each function. In your description, include the number of zeros, the
number of extrema, and the end behavior of the graph.

4. $f(x) = -x(x - a)^2$

5. $f(x) = (x + a)^2(x - b)^2$

6. $f(x) = x(x - a)(x + b)^3$

Assignment

Name _____ Date _____

The Wizard and the King
Introduction to Exponential Functions

You deposit $1000 into a savings account in which the interest is compounded annually at a rate of 5%.

1. Write an equation that represents the principal after t years.

2. What is the principal after 5 years?

3. What is the principal after 10 years?

4. What is the principal after 20 years?

You deposit $2500 into a savings account in which the interest is compounded monthly at an annual rate of 1.5%.

5. Write an equation that represents the principal after t years.

6. What is the principal after 6 months?

7. What is the principal after 2 years?

8. What is the principal after 15 years?

Consider Account A and Account B, where Account A earns interest that is compounded annually and Account B earns interest that is compounded monthly. You want to deposit $2000 into one of these accounts for 20 years.

9. Suppose that Account A earns 8% interest compounded annually and Account B earns 7.5% interest compounded monthly. Which is the better choice—Account A or Account B? Explain your reasoning.

10. Suppose that Account A earns 12% interest compounded annually and Account B earns 11.5% interest compounded monthly. Which is the better choice—Account A or Account B? Explain your reasoning.

Use *The Rule of 72* to answer Questions 11 and 12.

11. About how long will it take for your balance to reach $2000 if you deposit $1000 into an account that earns 8% interest compounded annually?

12. About how long will it take for your balance to reach $1000 if you deposit $500 into an account that earns 6% interest compounded monthly?

6

Assignment

Name _____   Date _____

A Review
Properties of Whole Number Exponents

Expand the expression.

1. $5x^3$

2. $9y^6$

3. $7x^7y^2$

4. $20abc^{10}$

Use the definition of a power to rewrite the expression.

5. $2 \cdot x \cdot x \cdot x \cdot x$

6. $11 \cdot w \cdot w \cdot w \cdot w \cdot w \cdot w \cdot w \cdot w \cdot w$

7. $5 \cdot c \cdot c \cdot c \cdot c \cdot c \cdot d \cdot d$

8. $19 \cdot x \cdot x \cdot x \cdot y \cdot y \cdot y \cdot y \cdot y \cdot y \cdot z \cdot z \cdot z$

Simplify the expression.

9. $9z^8 + 4z^8$

10. $3x^3 + 12y^5 - x^3 - 3x^5 + 8y^5$

11. $2a^2 \cdot 4a^3 \cdot (-a^0)$

12. $5g \cdot (-h^2) \cdot (-3g^5) \cdot 4h^6$

6

13. $\dfrac{6xy}{8x^3y}$

14. $\dfrac{10a^5b^4}{2a^2b^3}$

15. $(x^5)^7$

16. $((w^2)^4)^3$

17. $(2s^3t)^4$

18. $(2x^5y^2)^3 \cdot (-5x^2y^3)^2$

19. $\left(\dfrac{2x^3}{y}\right)^4$

20. $\left(\dfrac{3a^5}{4b^2}\right)^2 \cdot \left(\dfrac{a^0}{b^4}\right)^3$

Assignment

Name _____ Date _____

Exponents, Reciprocals, and Roots
Integral and Rational Exponents

Rewrite the expression using positive exponents. Then simplify, if possible.

1. $3x^{-5}$

2. $(a^2b^{-8})^3$

3. $2x^2y^{-3} \cdot 5x^3y$

4. $\left(\dfrac{4s^6t^{-2}}{6s^{10}t^{-5}}\right)^{-1}$

Solve the equation for a. Then rewrite the original equation by substituting the value for a into the equation.

5. $3^a \cdot 3^a = 3$

6. $6^a \cdot 6^a \cdot 6^a \cdot 6^a \cdot 6^a = 6$

7. $(9^a)^3 = 81$

8. $64^a = 4$

Rewrite the expression without fractional exponents.

9. $5^{\frac{1}{4}}$

10. $2^{\frac{3}{5}}$

Rewrite the expression without radicals.

11. $\sqrt{6^5}$

12. $\sqrt[3]{10^7}$

Simplify the expression. Write your answer without radicals. Use positive fractional exponents, when necessary.

13. $\left(x^{\frac{1}{5}}\right)^4$

14. $x^{\frac{5}{6}} \cdot x^{\frac{1}{2}}$

15. $\sqrt[3]{x^2}\,\sqrt[9]{y^4}$

16. $\sqrt[4]{x^2 y^8}$

17. $\left(8^{\frac{3}{5}}\,x^{\frac{3}{4}}\right)^{-5}$

18. $\left(27x^2 y^{\frac{1}{4}}\right)^{\frac{2}{3}}$

19. $\sqrt[3]{xy^8} \cdot \sqrt{81x^6 y^2}$

20. $\sqrt{(4x^3 y)^3} \cdot \sqrt{16xy^8}$

6

Assignment

Name _____ Date _____

The Hockey Stick Graph
Applications of Exponential Functions

Write an equation to model the situation.

1. You buy a new car for $18,000. The value of the car depreciates at a rate of about 20% per year. Write an equation that represents the value V of the car after y years.

2. A town's population is 78,400 in 1990. The population has been growing at a rate of 2.5% each year. Write an equation that represents the town's population P where t represents the number of years after 1990.

3. A radioactive element has a half-life of 240 years. There are 750 grams of the element. Write an equation that represents the amount of radioactive material left, N, after t years.

A scientist is studying a colony of insects. The insect population increases at a rate of about 30% per month. The scientist began his study with 22 insects.

4. Use the formula for population growth or decline to model the problem situation. Let t be the time in months.

5. What is the insect population after 2 months?

6. What is the insect population after 8 months?

6

7. What is the insect population after 1 year?

8. What is the insect population after 16 months?

9. Use your answers from Questions 2–5 to complete the table. Use the values in the table to graph the function.

Time in Months, *t*	Population, *P*

10. Use the graph to estimate the number of months it takes for the population to reach 300.

11. Use the graph to estimate the number of months it takes for the population to reach 2000.

12. Use the graph to estimate the number of months it takes for the population to triple.

Assignment

Name _____ Date _____

Log a What?
Inverses of Exponential Functions: Logarithmic Functions

Convert the exponential equation to logarithmic form.

1. $2^x = 15$

2. $e^x = 1.5$

3. $5^{4x} = 22$

4. $9^{2x-5} = 6$

Convert the logarithmic equation to exponential form.

5. $x = \log_3 12$

6. $3x = \log_2 4$

7. $x - 1 = \log_7 30$

8. $x = \log_5 3 - 2$

Use the definition of a logarithm to write an expression for x.

9. $3^{5x} = 24$

10. $6^{x-1} = 12$

11. $4^{2x} = 8$

12. $2^{x+2} = 0.15$

6

Write the inverse of the function. Then complete a table of values for the given function and a table of values for the inverse function. Use the tables of values to graph both functions on the same grid.

13. $f(x) = 4^x$

$f^{-1}(x) =$ _____

x	f(x)
−2	
0	
1	
2	
3	

x	$f^{-1}(x)$
$\frac{1}{16}$	
$\frac{1}{4}$	
1	
4	
16	

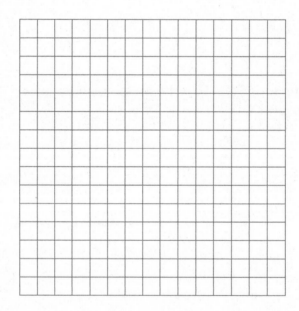

6

14. $f(x) = \log_5 x$

$f^{-1}(x) =$ _____

x	f(x)
$\frac{1}{5}$	
1	
5	
25	
125	

x	f⁻¹(x)
−1	
0	
1	
2	
3	

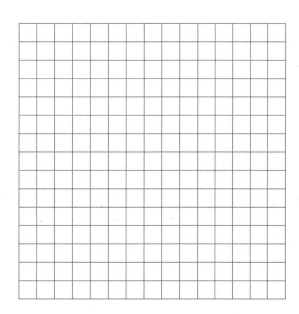

6

Assignment

Name _____ Date _____

Properties of Logarithms
Deriving the Properties of Logarithms

Complete each statement.

1. $\log_x x =$ _____

2. $\log_a xy =$ _____ + _____

3. $\log_a \dfrac{x}{y} =$ _____ − _____

4. $\log_b a =$ _____ ÷ _____

Rewrite the logarithm using common logs. Then evaluate using a calculator. Check your answer.

5. $\log_4 9$ 6. $\log_8 48$

7. $\log_3 0.25$ 8. $\log_5 16.62$

Write the logarithmic expression in expanded form.

9. $\log_2 5x$ 10. $\log_7 3x^4$

11. $\log_6 \dfrac{x^2}{y^3}$ 12. $\log_4 \dfrac{2x^5}{9y}$

Write the logarithmic expression using a single logarithm.

13. $\log_3 4 + 2\log_3 x$

14. $3\log_5 x - 5\log_5 y$

15. $2(\ln 4 + \ln x)$

16. $\log_4 6 + 7\log_4 x - 2\log_4 y$

17. $3(4\log_8 x + 5\log_8 y)$

18. $2\ln x + 2(3\ln y - 5\ln z)$

Assignment

Name _____ Date _____

Continuous Growth, Decay, and Interest
Solving Exponential and Logarithmic Equations

Solve the equation.

1. $6 = 0.5^x$

2. $1.5 = 10^{x-2}$

3. $3 = e^{4x}$

4. $426 = 3^{5x}$

5. A city's population was 1,250,000 in 2006. The population is expected to decrease at a rate of 1.75% each year.

  a. Write an equation to represent the city's population P where t represents the number of years after 2006.

  b. In what year will the city's population be 750,000?

c. In what year will the city's population be half of what it was in 2006?

6. You deposit $3200 into an account that earns 6.2% interest, compounded continuously.

a. Write an equation to represent the principal P after t years.

b. How long does it take for the investment to increase by 50%?

c. How long does it take for the investment to triple?

7. Radium-226 is a radioactive element with a half-life of 1600 years.

   a. Write an equation that you can use to determine the decay constant, k, for radium-226.

   b. Solve the equation for k.

   c. Calculate the approximate number of radium-226 atoms that decay each year.

6

6

Assignment

Name _____ Date _____

Cars and Growing Old
Introduction to Rational Functions

You are making punch for the school social. You decide to combine apple juice and raspberry juice to make apple-raspberry punch. You want to make a total of 10 liters of punch.

1. If the ratio of apple juice to raspberry juice in the punch is 1, how many liters of each type of juice are in the punch?

2. If the ratio of apple juice to raspberry juice in the punch is 0.25, how many liters of each type of juice are in the punch?

3. If the ratio of apple juice to raspberry juice in the punch is 1.5, how many liters of each type of juice are in the punch?

4. Let x represent the number of liters of apple juice in the punch. Write an expression to represent the number of liters of raspberry juice in the punch.

5. Write a function that represents the ratio of the number of liters of apple juice in the punch to the number of liters of raspberry juice in the punch.

6. Determine the domain and range for the problem situation. Then determine the domain and range for the mathematical function. Are the domains and ranges the same? Why or why not?

7. Complete the table of values for the mathematical function you wrote in Question 5.

x	f(x)
−30	
−20	
−15	
−9	
−8	
−5	
−2	
0	

x	f(x)
2	
5	
0	
9	
12	
15	
20	
30	

8. Graph the function using the table of values from Question 7.

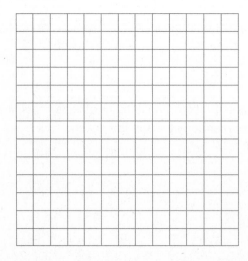

© 2008 Carnegie Learning, Inc.

7

Name_____ Date _____

9. What are the *x*- and *y*-intercepts?

10. What are the asymptotes?

11. Describe the end behavior of the graph.

Complete the table for the following functions. Then use the table to graph the function. Determine the domain and range of the function. Then determine the asymptotes, if any.

12. $f(x) = \dfrac{5}{x}$

x	f(x)
−10	
−5	
−2	
−1	
0	
2	
3	
5	
10	

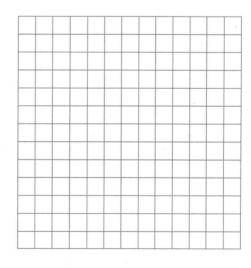

Domain:

Range:

Asymptote(s):

13. $f(x) = \dfrac{x}{x + 100}$

x	f(x)
−400	
−200	
−150	
−125	
−75	
−50	
0	
100	
200	

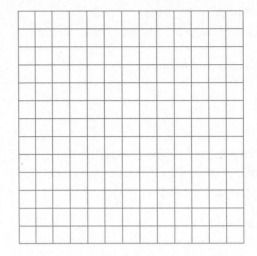

Domain:

Range:

Asymptote(s):

7

Assignment

Name _____ Date _____

Rational Expressions, Part I
Simplifying, Adding, and Subtracting Rational Expressions

Simplify the expression. Be sure to list any restrictions for the variables.

1. $\dfrac{8x^2yz^3}{40xy^3z^4}$

2. $\dfrac{16a^3bcd^3}{6ab^2c}$

3. $\dfrac{4cd - 8c}{d^2 - 4}$

4. $\dfrac{2x^3 - 6x^2 + 8x}{6x^2 - 12x}$

5. $\dfrac{8(z + 1)^3}{24z^2 + 4z - 20}$

6. $\dfrac{4y^3 + 8y^2 - 9y - 18}{2y^2 + 7y + 6}$

Add or subtract. Write the answer in simplest form. Be sure to list any restrictions for the variable.

7. $\dfrac{2a}{5} + \dfrac{5}{6} + \dfrac{13b}{15}$

8. $\dfrac{3}{4x^2 - 1} + \dfrac{7}{2x - 1}$

9. $\dfrac{2}{n + 6} - \dfrac{4n}{n^2 + 3n - 18}$

10. $\dfrac{x - 4}{x^2 - 7x + 12} + \dfrac{3}{x^2 - x - 6}$

11. $\dfrac{-5x + 2}{4x^2 - 49} - \dfrac{1}{(6x + 21)}$

12. $\dfrac{x - 2}{x^2 + 3x + 2} + \dfrac{x + 1}{x^2 - 4} - \dfrac{2}{x + 1}$

Name _____ Date _____

Rational Expressions, Part II
Multiplying and Dividing Rational Expressions

Multiply or divide. Write the product or quotient in simplest form. Be sure to list any restrictions for the denominator.

1. $\dfrac{4t^3}{t + 5} \cdot \dfrac{3t^2 + 15t}{12t}$

2. $\dfrac{x - 8}{3x^2} \cdot \dfrac{18x^2}{-2x + 16}$

3. $\dfrac{x + 3}{2x^2 - 3x - 2} \cdot \dfrac{6x^2 + 3x}{x^2 + 2x - 3}$

4. $\dfrac{4a + 20}{6a^3} \cdot \dfrac{6a^2 + 18}{a} \cdot \dfrac{a^5}{7a^2 + 35a}$

5. $\dfrac{24xy^2}{x^2 - 4} \cdot \dfrac{x^2 - 3x - 10}{4x^2y - 20xy}$

6. $\dfrac{2pq}{7} \cdot \dfrac{28p + 21}{q^2 + q} \cdot \dfrac{q^2 - 1}{8p + 6}$

7

7. $\dfrac{12}{5ab} \div \dfrac{8b^2}{15a}$

8. $\dfrac{3x - 1}{14x^3} \div \dfrac{27x^2 - 3}{21x}$

9. $\dfrac{36 - w^2}{6w^2 + 66w} \div \dfrac{-5w - 30}{30w}$

10. $\dfrac{2y^2}{2yz + 6y} \div \dfrac{10yz^3}{2z^2 + 14z + 24}$

11. $\dfrac{10rs}{r^3 - rs^2} \div \dfrac{8r^2s}{r^2 + rs}$

12. $\dfrac{2c^2d + 2cd}{c^2 + 2c + 1} \div \dfrac{4c^3 + 4c^2}{5c + 5}$

Assignment

Name _____ Date _____

Solutions
Solving Rational Equations and Inequalities

Solve the equations and check the solutions. Be sure to list any extraneous solutions or any restrictions to the solution set.

1. $\dfrac{9}{x} + 14 = \dfrac{30}{x}$

2. $\dfrac{x + 8}{x - 11} = 1$

3. $\dfrac{x^2 + 6x}{9} = \dfrac{4x}{3}$

4. $\dfrac{2x^3 - x + 12}{6} = \dfrac{x^3 + 5}{3}$

5. $-\dfrac{3}{x} + \dfrac{x}{5} - \dfrac{2x}{5} = -\dfrac{3}{10}$

6. $\dfrac{4x}{3} - \dfrac{12}{x} - \dfrac{5x}{4} = \dfrac{7}{12}$

7

7. $\dfrac{2x}{x+1} + \dfrac{9}{x-4} = \dfrac{45}{x^2 - 3x - 4}$

Solve the inequality.

8. $\dfrac{15}{x+27} < -3$

9. $\dfrac{4}{x+3} \geq \dfrac{8}{x}$

7

10. $\dfrac{16}{x+2} - \dfrac{36}{2x+4} > \dfrac{1}{x^2-4}$

Assignment

Name _____ Date _____

Holes and Breaks
Graphing Rational Functions and Discontinuities

List any removable and nonremovable discontinuities of the rational function.

1. $f(x) = \dfrac{x - 5}{x + 1}$

2. $g(x) = \dfrac{x - 2}{x^2 + 3x - 10}$

3. $h(x) = \dfrac{4}{x^2 + 3x + 2}$

4. $f(x) = \dfrac{x^2 + 11x + 28}{x + 7}$

List the removable discontinuity of the function. Then rewrite the function as a piecewise function to remove the discontinuity.

5. $r(x) = \dfrac{x - 3}{(x + 1)(x - 3)}$

6. $t(x) = \dfrac{(x + 4)(x - 6)}{(x + 4)}$

7. $w(x) = \dfrac{x}{3x^2 + 10x}$

8. $q(x) = \dfrac{x^2 - 12x + 27}{x - 3}$

Graph the rational function. List the domain, range, asymptote(s), and any removable and nonremovable discontinuities. If the function has any removable discontinuities, rewrite the function as a piecewise function to remove them.

9. $c(x) = \dfrac{x + 4}{x - 3}$

Domain:

Range:

Asymptote(s):

Removable discontinuity:

Nonremovable discontinuity:

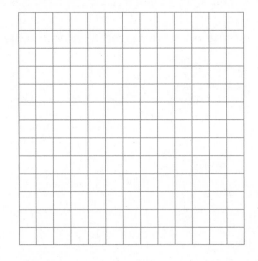

10. $p(x) = \dfrac{x + 2}{x^2 - 4x - 12}$

Domain:

Range:

Asymptote(s):

Removable discontinuity:

Nonremovable discontinuity:

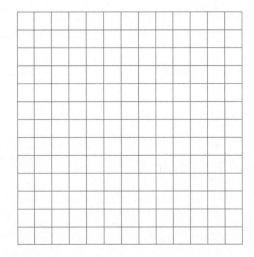

7

11. $k(x) = \dfrac{x^2 - 3x - 4}{x^2 - 4x}$

Domain:

Range:

Asymptote(s):

Removable discontinuity:

Nonremovable discontinuity:

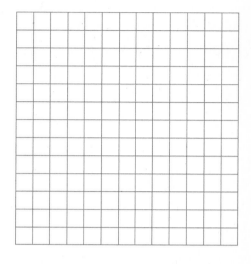

12. $f(x) = \dfrac{2x^2 - 7x - 15}{2x + 3}$

Domain:

Range:

Asymptote(s):

Removable discontinuity:

Nonremovable discontinuity:

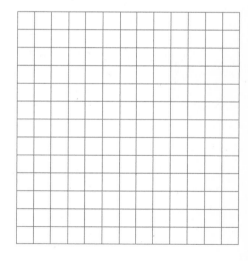

7

Assignment

Assignment for Lesson 7.6

Name _____ Date _____

Work, Mixture, and More
Applications of Rational Equations and Functions

Two teams of construction workers have been contracted to build an addition for your school library. If Team A works alone, they can complete the job in 32 days. If Team B works alone, they can complete the job in 20 days.

1. How much of the job can Team A complete in x days? How much of the job can Team B complete in x days? Which team can complete more of the job in the same number of days?

2. Suppose that Team A and Team B work together for x days. How much of the job can they complete in x days?

3. Write and solve an equation to calculate the number of days it would take both teams working together to complete the job.

© 2008 Carnegie Learning, Inc.

7

Chapter 7 ● Assignments **147**

A 250-milliliter acid solution contains 35% acid.

4. What would be the acid concentration if you added 30 milliliters of water to the solution? What would be the acid concentration if you added 100 milliliters of water to the solution?

5. Write a function to represent the fractional concentration $C(x)$ of the solution when x millimeters of water is added to the solution.

6. How much water should you add to the solution if you want a 10% acid solution?

You buy a new fish tank for $800. It is estimated to cost about $125 each year to own including cleaning supplies, electricity, food, etc.

7. Assuming that these estimates are reliable, what is the average annual cost if you have the fish tank for 5 years? 10 years? 20 years?

7

8. Write a function that shows the average annual cost $C(x)$ of the fish tank over x years.

9. How many years did you have the fish tank if the average annual cost was $225?

10. Graph the function. Determine the domain, range, asymptotes, discontinuities, and end behavior of the function.

Domain:

Range:

Asymptotes:

Discontinuities:

End behavior:

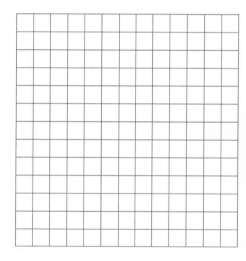

7

7

Assignment

Name _____   Date _____

Inverses of Inverses
Introduction to Radical Functions and Expressions

Evaluate the expression.

1. $-\sqrt{121}$

2. $\sqrt[5]{5} - 1$

3. $\sqrt[4]{a^4}$

4. $\sqrt[3]{x^9 y^6}$

Determine whether the given graph represents a function.

5.

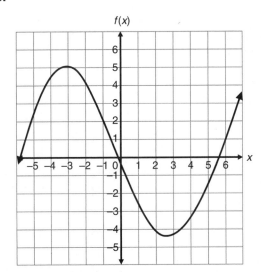

6.

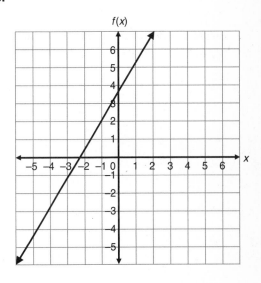

7.

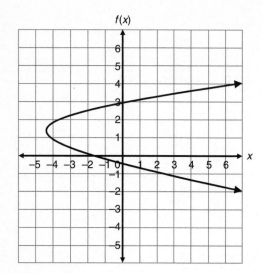

8.

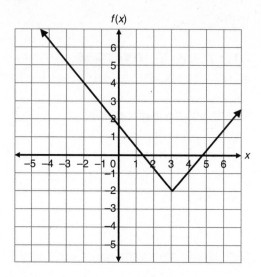

Write the inverse of the function and graph both $f(x)$ and $f^{-1}(x)$ on the same grid. Then determine whether $f^{-1}(x)$ is a function.

9. $f(x) = x^3 + 1$

10. $f(x) = \sqrt[4]{x}$

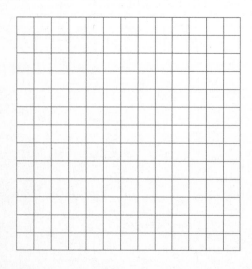

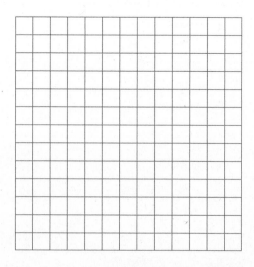

11. $f(x) = 2x^4 - 4$

12. $f(x) = 3\sqrt[5]{x} - 1$

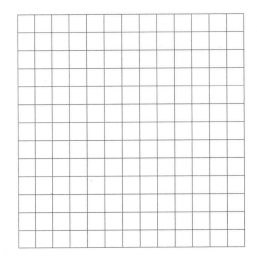

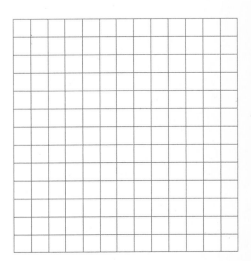

8

8

Assignment

Name _____ Date _____

Radical Expressions
Simplifying and Operating with Radical Expressions

Simplify the expression.

1. $\sqrt{a^4b^{10}}$

2. $\sqrt[3]{8x^6y^3}$

3. $\sqrt{(c+7)^4}$

4. $\sqrt[4]{256x^4y^{20}z^{12}}$

5. $-\sqrt{20y^9}$

6. $\sqrt{18m^3n^6}$

7. $-\sqrt[4]{a^2b^6c^{12}}$

8. $\sqrt[3]{24(x+y)^5}$

Perform the indicated operation(s) and simplify.

9. $9\sqrt{y}\left(5\sqrt{y} - \sqrt{y}\right)$

10. $a^2 \cdot \left(2\sqrt{b}\right)^4$

11. $3\sqrt[4]{w} + 5\sqrt[4]{w} - 11\sqrt[4]{w}$

12. $-5\sqrt[3]{x}\left(\sqrt[3]{x^6} + 2x^3\right)$

13. $8.2\sqrt[4]{c^2 d^8} - 6.5\sqrt[4]{c^5 d^4}$

14. $\sqrt[5]{x^2 y^4} \cdot \sqrt[3]{x^3} \cdot \sqrt[5]{y^9}$

15. $\dfrac{-7\sqrt[4]{x}}{5\sqrt[3]{x}}$

16. $\dfrac{\left(3\sqrt{x^7 y^4}\right)\left(\sqrt[3]{-8x^6 y^4}\right)}{\sqrt{9x^3 y^{10}}}$

Assignment

Name _____ Date _____

Solutions
Solving Radical Equations

Solve the equation and check your solution.

1. $\sqrt{3x} - 10 = -4$

2. $\sqrt{6x + 7} = 2$

3. $5\sqrt[3]{2 + x} = 20$

4. $\sqrt[4]{4x - 9} + 2 = 3$

5. $x - \sqrt{x - 3} = 3$

6. $x = \sqrt{4 - x} - 2$

8

7. $2 + \sqrt[3]{12x - 6x^2} = x$

8. $\sqrt[3]{1 - x^3} + x = 1$

Use the Distance Formula to find the point(s). Check your answer(s).

9. Find the point(s) on the x-axis that is (are) 8 units from the point (2, 6).

10. Find the point(s) on the y-axis that is 10 units from the point (–1, 4).

8

11. Find the point(s) on the line $x = -6$ that is 5 units from the point $(-3, -2)$.

12. Find the point(s) on the line $y = 4$ that is 16 units from the point $(5, -8)$.

8

Assignment

Name _____ Date _____

Graphs
Graphing Radical Functions

Describe the transformation(s) on the parent function $y = \sqrt{x}$ that produces the graph of the given function, where a is a positive integer.

1. $f(x) = \sqrt{x} + a$

2. $g(x) = \sqrt{x - a}$

3. $t(x) = \sqrt{x}$

4. $v(x) = \sqrt{ax}$

5. $h(x) = \sqrt{x} - a$

6. $q(x) = \sqrt{-x + a}$

Graph the function and determine the domain, range, and zero(s). Then describe the transformations on the parent function that produce the graph of the given function.

7. $f(x) = \sqrt{x} + 5$

Domain:

Range:

Zero(s):

8. $h(x) = \dfrac{5\sqrt{x}}{2}$

Domain:

Range:

Zero(s):

8

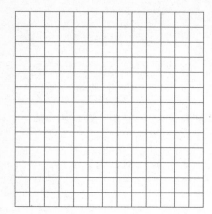

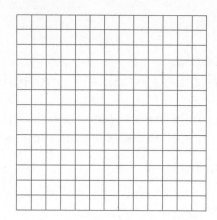

9. $k(x) = \sqrt[3]{8x}$

Domain:

Range:

Zero(s):

10. $p(x) = \sqrt[4]{-x} - 1$

Domain:

Range:

Zero(s):

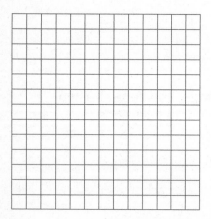

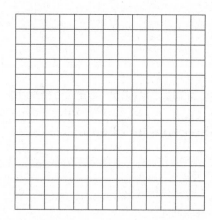

8

Assignment

Name _____ Date _____

9

Conics?
Conic Sections

Determine the conic section that results from the intersection of the double-napped cone shown and each plane described.

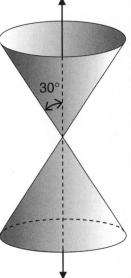

1. A plane that passes through one nappe of the double-napped cone and is perpendicular to the axis of the cone

   The intersection is a _____.

2. A plane that passes through one nappe of the double-napped cone and is parallel to the edge of the cone

   The intersection is a _____.

3. A plane that passes through both nappes of the double-napped cone and is parallel to the axis of the cone

   The intersection is a _____.

4. A plane that passes through one nappe of the double-napped cone and is at an angle of 50° from the axis of the cone

   The intersection is an _____.

Match each conic section with a possible equation of that conic.

5. circle

    a. $\dfrac{x^2}{9} + \dfrac{y^2}{64} = 1$

6. parabola

    b. $\dfrac{x^2}{4} - \dfrac{y^2}{16} = 1$

7. ellipse

    c. $(x - 2)^2 + (y + 3)^2 = 5^2$

8. hyperbola

    d. $(x + 1)^2 = y - 3$

9

Assignment

Name _____ Date _____

Round and Round
Circles

Rewrite the equation of the circle in standard form. Then identify the center and radius of the circle.

1. $y^2 = 36 - x^2$

2. $2y^2 - 10 = -2x^2$

3. $\dfrac{x^2 + y^2}{2} = 1$

4. $4x^2 = 4(50 - y^2)$

5. $x^2 + y^2 - 6x - 7 = 0$

6. $x^2 + y^2 + 2x + 2y = 7$

7. $x^2 + y^2 = 4 + 4y$

8. $x^2 + 10x = 74 + 2y - y^2$

Identify the center and radius of the circle shown. Then write the equation of the circle in standard form.

9.

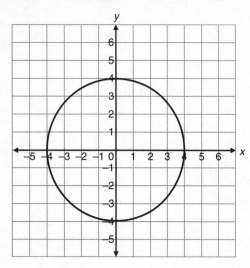

10.

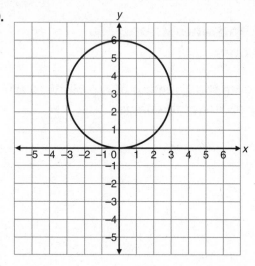

11.

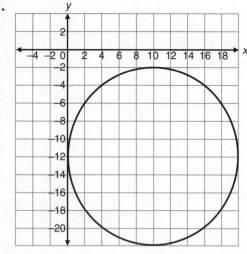

12.

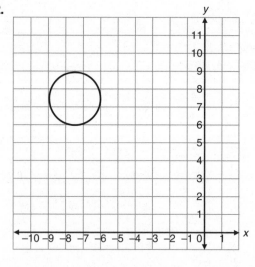

Assignment

Name _____ Date _____

It's a Stretch
Ellipses

Use the equation of the ellipse to identify the center, vertices, foci, eccentricity, minor axis endpoints, and the lengths of the minor and major axes.

1. $\dfrac{x^2}{25} + \dfrac{y^2}{9} = 1$

      Center:

      Vertices:

      Foci:

      Eccentricity:

      Minor axis endpoints:

      Minor axis length:

      Major axis length:

2. $\dfrac{x^2}{5} + \dfrac{y^2}{16} = 1$

      Center:

      Vertices:

      Foci:

      Eccentricity:

      Minor axis endpoints:

      Minor axis length:

      Major axis length:

3. $\dfrac{(x-3)^2}{4} + \dfrac{(y+2)^2}{9} = 1$

      Center:

      Vertices:

      Foci:

      Eccentricity:

      Minor axis endpoints:

      Minor axis length:

      Major axis length:

4. $\dfrac{(x+4)^2}{40} + \dfrac{(y+1)^2}{36} = 1$

      Center:

      Vertices:

      Foci:

      Eccentricity:

      Minor axis endpoints:

      Minor axis length:

      Major axis length:

Identify the center, vertices, and lengths of the major and minor axes of the ellipse shown. Then write the equation of the ellipse in standard form.

5.

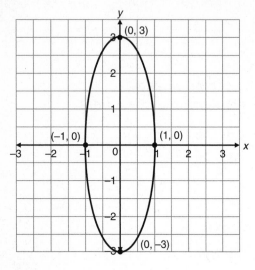

6.

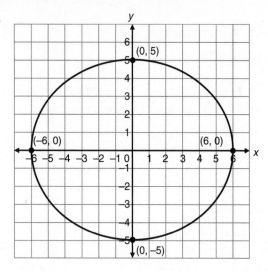

Center:

Vertices:

Length of major axis:

Length of minor axis:

Equation:

Center:

Vertices:

Length of major axis:

Length of minor axis:

Equation:

7.

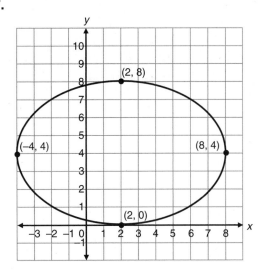

8.

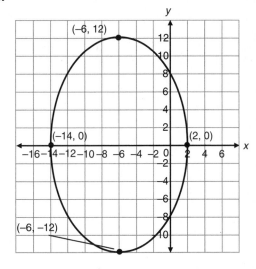

Center:

Vertices:

Length of major axis:

Length of minor axis:

Equation:

Center:

Vertices:

Length of major axis:

Length of minor axis:

Equation:

Rewrite the equation of the ellipse in standard form. Then graph the ellipse and label the center, vertices, and minor axis endpoints.

9. $y^2 = 1 - \dfrac{x^2}{4}$

10. $x^2 + 4y^2 = 100$

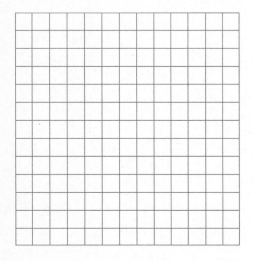

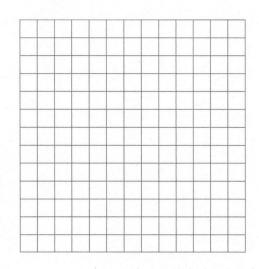

11. $9(x + 1)^2 + 7(y + 5)^2 = 63$

12. $(x - 2)^2 = 225 - \dfrac{9(y + 2)^2}{16}$

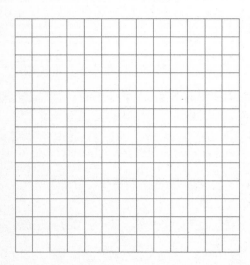

Assignment

Name _____   Date _____

9

More Asymptotes
Hyperbolas

Use the equation of the hyperbola to identify the center, vertices, foci, eccentricity, minor axis endpoints, and the lengths of the minor and major axes.

1. $\dfrac{y^2}{16} - \dfrac{x^2}{9} = 1$

Center:

Vertices:

Foci:

Eccentricity:

Minor axis endpoints:

Minor axis length:

Major axis length:

2. $\dfrac{(x + 5)^2}{121} - \dfrac{(y - 8)^2}{81} = 1$

Center:

Vertices:

Foci:

Eccentricity:

Minor axis endpoints:

Minor axis length:

Major axis length:

3. $\dfrac{x^2}{6} - \dfrac{(y + 12)^2}{25} = 1$

Center:

Vertices:

Foci:

Eccentricity:

Minor axis endpoints:

Minor axis length:

Major axis length:

4. $\dfrac{(y - 7)^2}{100} - \dfrac{(x - 2)^2}{200} = 1$

Center:

Vertices:

Foci:

Eccentricity:

Minor axis endpoints:

Minor axis length:

Major axis length:

Identify the center, vertices, and lengths of the major and minor axes of the sketch of the hyperbola shown. Then write the equation of the hyperbola in standard form.

5.

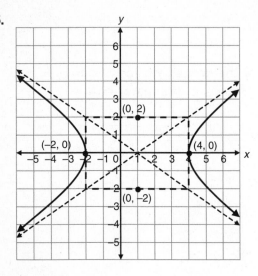

Center:

Vertices:

Length of major axis:

Length of minor axis:

Equation:

6.

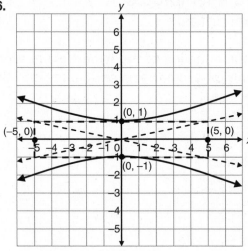

Center:

Vertices:

Length of major axis:

Length of minor axis:

Equation:

Name_____ Date _____

7.

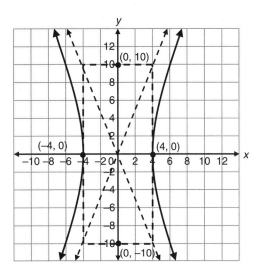

Center: _____

Vertices: _____

Length of major axis: _____

Length of minor axis: _____

Equation: _____

8.

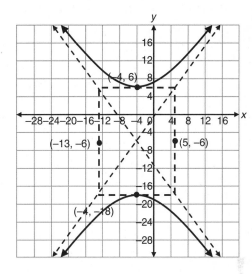

Center: _____

Vertices: _____

Length of major axis: _____

Length of minor axis: _____

Equation: _____

Rewrite the equation of the hyperbola in standard form. Then graph the hyperbola and label the center, vertices, and minor axis endpoints.

9. $4y^2 = 25x^2 + 100$

10. $2y^2 - x^2 + 4 = 20$

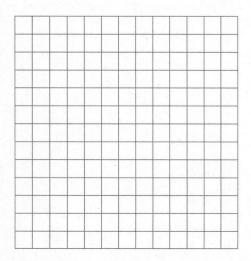

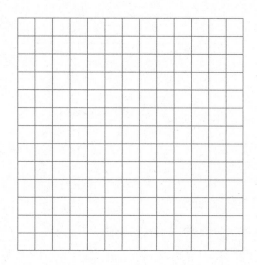

11. $(x - 4)^2 - 9 = (y - 2)^2$

12. $9(x - 5)^2 - 4(y + 3)^2 - 144 = 0$

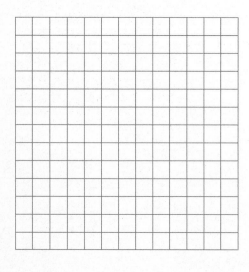

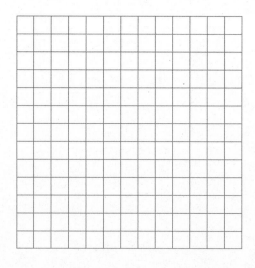

Assignment

Name _____ Date _____

Ultimate Focus
Parabolas

Use the equation of the parabola to identify the vertex, focus, equation of the directrix, and the equation of the line of symmetry.

1. $y^2 = -4x$

Vertex:

Focus:

Directrix:

Line of symmetry:

2. $y = (x - 3)^2$

Vertex:

Focus:

Directrix:

Line of symmetry:

3. $(x + 2)^2 = 8(y - 6)$

Vertex:

Focus:

Directrix:

Line of symmetry:

4. $(y + 8)^2 = -3(x + 5)$

Vertex:

Focus:

Directrix:

Line of symmetry:

The graph of a parabola and its vertex and focus are shown. Write the equation of the parabola in standard form.

5.

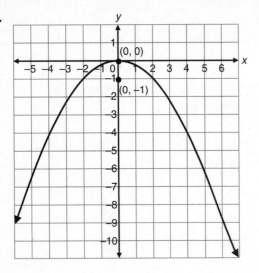

6.

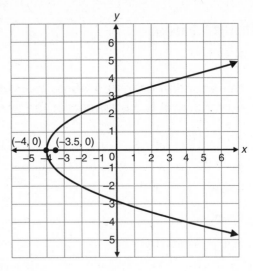

7.

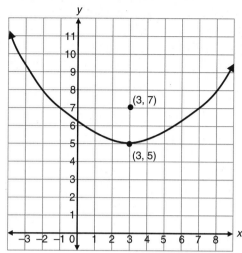

8.

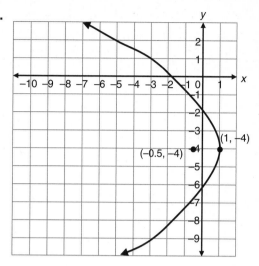

Rewrite the equation of the parabola in standard form. Then graph the parabola and label the vertex, focus, and the line of symmetry.

9. $y^2 + 6y + 8x + 9 = 0$

10. $x = \dfrac{y^2}{4}$

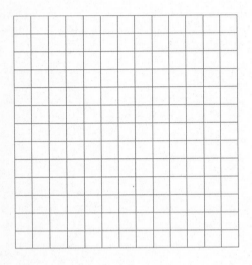
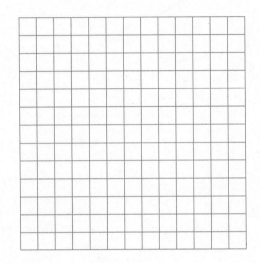

11. $x^2 - 4x - 12y - 20 = 0$

12. $x^2 + 2x = -2y - 11$

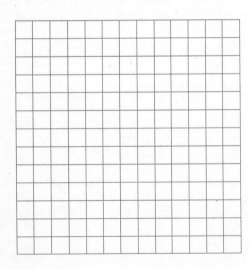

Assignment

Assignment for Lesson 9.6

Name _____ Date _____

Antennas, Whispering Rooms, and More
Applications of Conics

Some comets follow a path that is in the shape of an ellipse. One such comet is called *Comet Wild 2*. The distance between the vertices of the ellipse that models its path is approximately 6.88 AU (astronomical units) and the eccentricity is approximately 0.54.

Use this information to answer the following questions. Round all answers to the nearest thousandths, if necessary.

1. What are the coordinates of the vertices of the ellipse that models the path of *Comet Wild 2*? Let the ellipse be centered at (0, 0).

2. What are the coordinates of the foci?

3. What are the coordinates of the co-vertices?

4. What is the distance between the co-vertices?

5. Write an equation for the ellipse that models the path of *Comet Wild 2*.

6. Graph the ellipse that models the path of *Comet Wild 2*. Label the vertices, co-vertices, and foci.

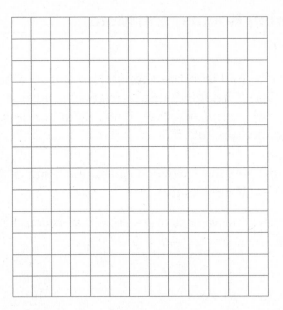

A cable between two towers on the Golden Gate Bridge in San Francisco can be modeled by the equation of a parabola. The distance between the towers is about 4200 feet and the height of each tower is about 500 feet, as shown in the figure.

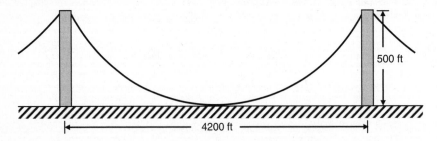

500 ft

4200 ft

Use this information and the figure to answer the following questions.

7. Name three points that lie on the parabola that models the cable.

8. Use the regression feature of a graphing calculator to determine the equation of the parabola. Do not round your answer.

9. Write the equation of the parabola in standard form. What is the value of p?

10. Graph the parabola that models the cable.

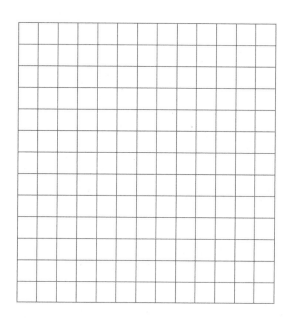

9

Assignment

Name _____ Date _____

The Unit Circle
Angle Measures

Sketch the angle in standard position with the given measure on the graph.

1. 45°

2. −160°

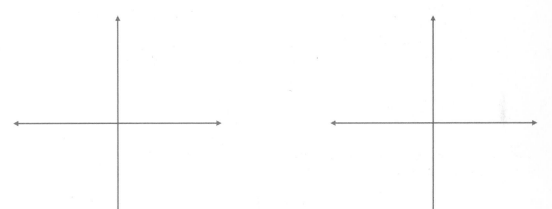

3. 1.25 revolutions clockwise

4. $\frac{\pi}{6}$ radian

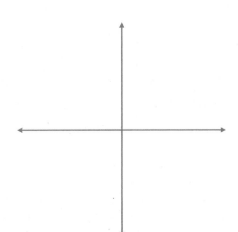

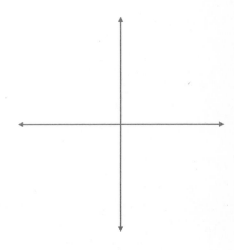

Each angle measure is given in revolutions. Write the angle measure in degrees and radians.

5. three revolutions counter-clockwise

6. 0.25 revolution counter-clockwise

7. $1\frac{2}{3}$ revolutions counter-clockwise

8. $\frac{5}{6}$ revolution counter-clockwise

Each angle measure is given in degrees. Write the angle measure in revolutions and radians.

9. 120°

10. 260°

11. 5°

12. 860°

Each angle measure is given in radians. Write the angle measure in revolutions and degrees.

13. $\dfrac{\pi}{3}$ radian

14. $\dfrac{5\pi}{4}$ radian

15. $\dfrac{\pi}{72}$ radian

16. $\dfrac{2\pi}{45}$ radian

10

Assignment

Name _____ Date _____

Circular Functions, Part I
Sine and Cosine Functions

Use a calculator to evaluate the expression. Make sure the calculator is in radian mode. Round your answer to the nearest ten-thousandth, if necessary.

1. $\sin \dfrac{\pi}{6}$

2. $\sin\left(\dfrac{\pi}{6} + 2\pi\right)$

3. $\sin \dfrac{\pi}{4}$

4. $\sin\left(\dfrac{\pi}{4} + 2\pi\right)$

5. $\sin \dfrac{2\pi}{3}$

6. $\sin\left(\dfrac{2\pi}{3} + 2\pi\right)$

7. $\sin \dfrac{\pi}{2}$

8. $\sin\left(\dfrac{\pi}{2} + 2\pi\right)$

9. Based on your answers to Questions 1–8, write a rule that shows the relationship between $\sin \theta$ and $\sin(\theta + 2\pi)$.

Use a calculator to evaluate the expression. Make sure the calculator is in radian mode. Round your answers to the nearest ten-thousandths, if necessary.

10. $\sin \dfrac{\pi}{6}$

11. $\sin\left(\dfrac{\pi}{6} + \pi\right)$

12. $\sin \dfrac{\pi}{4}$

13. $\sin\left(\dfrac{\pi}{4} + \pi\right)$

14. $\sin \dfrac{2\pi}{3}$

15. $\sin \left(\dfrac{2\pi}{3} + \pi \right)$

16. $\sin \dfrac{\pi}{2}$

17. $\sin \left(\dfrac{\pi}{2} + \pi \right)$

18. Based on your answers to Questions 10–17, write a rule that shows the relationship between $\sin \theta$ and $\sin(\theta + \pi)$.

Use a calculator to evaluate the expression. Make sure the calculator is in radian mode. Round your answers to the nearest ten-thousandths, if necessary.

19. $\cos \dfrac{\pi}{3}$

20. $\cos \left(\dfrac{\pi}{3} + 2\pi \right)$

21. $\cos \dfrac{3\pi}{4}$

22. $\cos \left(\dfrac{3\pi}{4} + 2\pi \right)$

23. $\cos \dfrac{5\pi}{6}$

24. $\cos \left(\dfrac{5\pi}{6} + 2\pi \right)$

25. $\cos \dfrac{\pi}{2}$

26. $\cos \left(\dfrac{\pi}{2} + 2\pi \right)$

27. Based on your answers to Questions 19–26, write a rule that shows the relationship between $\cos \theta$ and $\cos(\theta + 2\pi)$.

Use a calculator to evaluate the expression. Make sure the calculator is in radian mode. Round your answers to the nearest ten-thousandths, if necessary.

28. $\cos\dfrac{\pi}{3}$

29. $\cos\left(\dfrac{\pi}{3} + \pi\right)$

30. $\cos\dfrac{3\pi}{4}$

31. $\cos\left(\dfrac{3\pi}{4} + \pi\right)$

32. $\cos\dfrac{5\pi}{6}$

33. $\cos\left(\dfrac{5\pi}{6} + \pi\right)$

34. $\cos\dfrac{\pi}{2}$

35. $\cos\left(\dfrac{\pi}{2} + \pi\right)$

36. Based on your answers to Questions 28–35, write a rule that shows the relationship between $\cos\theta$ and $\cos(\theta + \pi)$.

10

Assignment

Name _____ Date _____

Circular Functions, Part II
Tangent Function

Use a calculator to evaluate the expression. Make sure the calculator is in radian mode. Round your answers to the nearest ten-thousandths, if necessary.

1. $\tan \dfrac{\pi}{6}$

2. $\tan\left(\dfrac{\pi}{6} + \dfrac{\pi}{2}\right)$

3. $\tan \dfrac{\pi}{4}$

4. $\tan\left(\dfrac{\pi}{4} + \dfrac{\pi}{2}\right)$

5. $\tan \dfrac{\pi}{3}$

6. $\tan\left(\dfrac{\pi}{3} + \dfrac{\pi}{2}\right)$

7. $\tan \dfrac{2\pi}{3}$

8. $\tan\left(\dfrac{2\pi}{3} + \dfrac{\pi}{2}\right)$

9. $\tan \dfrac{3\pi}{4}$

10. $\tan\left(\dfrac{3\pi}{4} + \dfrac{\pi}{2}\right)$

11. $\tan \dfrac{5\pi}{6}$

12. $\tan\left(\dfrac{5\pi}{6} + \dfrac{\pi}{2}\right)$

13. $\tan \pi$

14. $\tan\left(\pi + \dfrac{\pi}{2}\right)$

15. Based on your answers to Questions 1–14, write a rule that shows the relationship between $\tan \theta$ and $\tan\left(\theta + \dfrac{\pi}{2}\right)$. $\left(\text{Hint: It may help to use the fact that } \tan \theta = \dfrac{\sin \theta}{\cos \theta} \text{ to write the tangent ratios in terms of } \sin \theta \text{ and } \cos \theta.\right)$

Assignment

Name _____ Date _____

You Mean There Are More?
Other Circular Functions

Write an equivalent equation for the given function's reciprocal function.

1. $\sin \theta = \dfrac{1}{2}$

2. $\tan \theta = 1$

3. $\cos \theta = -\dfrac{2}{3}$

4. $\tan \theta = \dfrac{5}{3}$

5. $\cos \theta = \dfrac{3}{4}$

6. $\sin \theta = -\dfrac{6}{7}$

7. $\cos \theta = -\dfrac{1}{5}$

8. $\tan \theta = 100$

Use the diagram to match each segment with the trigonometric expression that describes its length. Note: The circle in the diagram is a unit circle.

9. $\overline{UB}$ **a.** $\tan \theta$

10. $\overline{WX}$ **b.** $\cot \theta$

11. $\overline{YZ}$ **c.** $\sec \theta$

12. $\overline{OU}$ **d.** $\cos \theta$

13. $\overline{OX}$ **e.** $\sin \theta$

14. $\overline{OZ}$ **f.** $\csc \theta$

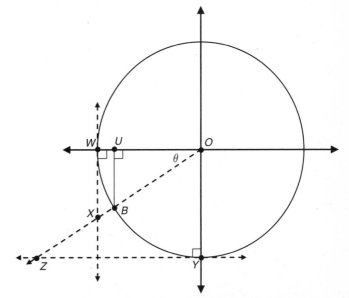

10

Assignment

Name _____ Date _____

Arc Functions
Inverses of Circular Functions

For each of the following, determine θ in degrees.

1. $\cos^{-1}\dfrac{1}{2} = \theta$

2. $\cot^{-1}(1) = \theta$

3. $\arcsin\dfrac{\sqrt{2}}{2} = \theta$

4. $\sec^{-1}(-2) = \theta$

For each of the following, determine x in radians.

5. $\sin^{-1}(-1) = x$

6. $\arctan -\dfrac{1}{\sqrt{3}} = x$

7. $\text{Arccsc(undefined)} = x$

8. $\sec^{-1}(\sqrt{2}) = x$

Use a calculator to determine the measure of θ in degrees. Round your answer to the nearest hundredth, if necessary.

9.

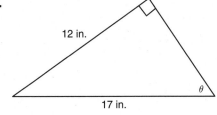

12 in.

17 in.

10.

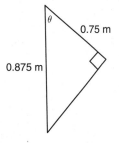

θ

0.75 m

0.875 m

11.

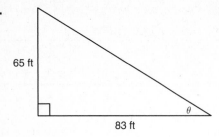

12.

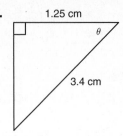

13. The Leaning Tower of Pisa is approximately 56 meters tall and leans so that the top of the tower is a horizontal distance of about 5 meters from the base, as shown in the diagram. Calculate the value of θ to determine the angle at which the tower leans. Round your answer to the nearest degree.

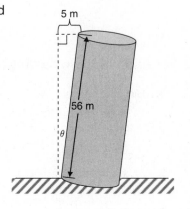

14. An airplane is descending as it prepares to land. The plane is currently at an altitude of 5000 feet, and the horizontal distance from the plane to the runway is 32,000 feet, as shown in the diagram. What is the angle of depression θ from the airplane to the runway? Round your answer to the nearest hundredth, if necessary.

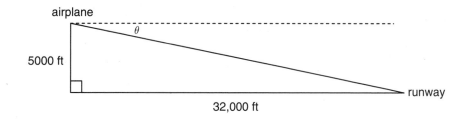

airplane

θ

5000 ft

32,000 ft

runway

15. A law requires that the ramp angle of a wheelchair ramp must be less than 4.8°. Is the wheelchair ramp represented in the diagram in compliance with the law?

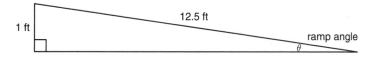

1 ft

12.5 ft

ramp angle

θ

Assignment

Name _____ Date _____

Ups and Downs
Graphs of Circular Functions

Sketch the graph of the function.

1. $f(x) = \sin x$

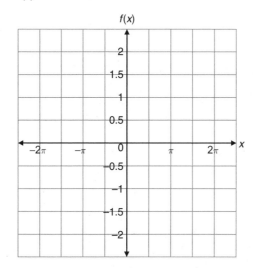

2. $f(x) = \cos x$

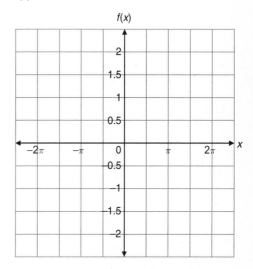

3. $f(x) = \tan x$

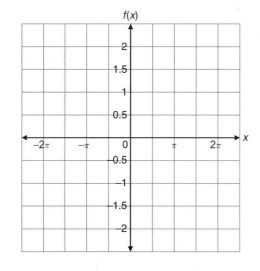

4. $f(x) = \csc x$

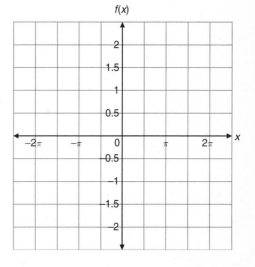

5. $f(x) = \sec x$

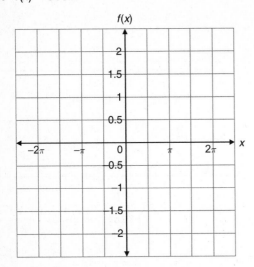

6. $f(x) = \cot x$

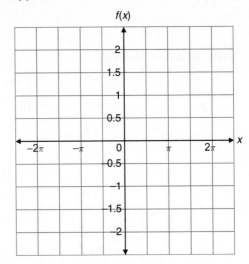

Use the graphs from Questions 1–6 to answer the following questions.

7. Which of the graphs, if any, have asymptotes?

8. Which of the graphs, if any, have a domain that includes all real numbers?

9. Which of the graphs, if any, have a range that includes all real numbers?

10. Which of the graphs, if any, have a restricted domain?

11. Which of the graphs, if any, have a restricted range?

12. Which of the graphs, if any, have a period of 2π?

13. Which of the graphs, if any, have a period of π?

14. Which of the graphs, if any, have a period of $\frac{\pi}{2}$?

15. Write the domains and ranges of all six functions.

© 2008 Carnegie Learning, Inc.

11

Assignment

Name _____ Date _____

Transformations
Amplitude, Period, Phase Shift

Write the equation of the function given its basic function and its graph. Describe the transformations on the basic function that produce the given graph.

1. basic function: $f(x) = \cos x$

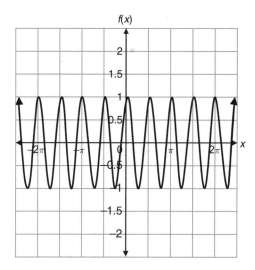

2. basic function: $f(x) = \sin x$

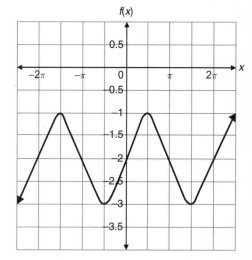

3. basic function: $f(x) = \sin x$

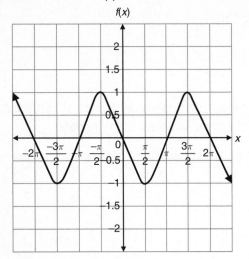

4. basic function: $f(x) = \cos x$

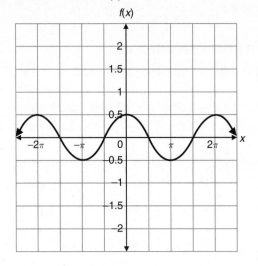

5. basic function: $f(x) = \sin x$

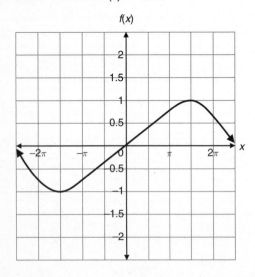

6. basic function: $f(x) = \cos x$

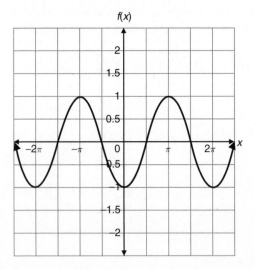

Name_____ Date _____

Graph the function and determine its minimum value, maximum value, amplitude, period, and frequency.

7. $f(x) = \sin(3x)$

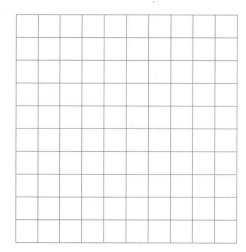

Minimum value:

Maximum value:

Amplitude:

Period:

Frequency:

8. $f(x) = 2\cos x$

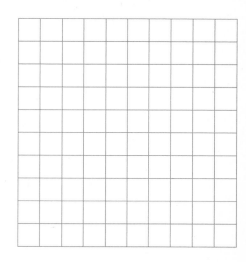

Minimum value:

Maximum value:

Amplitude:

Period:

Frequency:

9. $f(x) = -2 + \cos\left(x + \dfrac{\pi}{2}\right)$

10. $f(x) = 3 \sin\left(\dfrac{1}{4}x\right)$

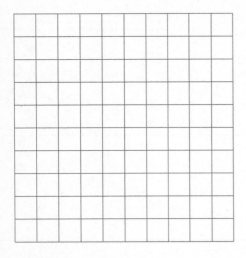

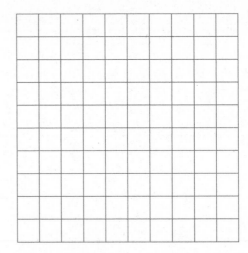

Minimum value:

Maximum value:

Amplitude:

Period:

Frequency:

Minimum value:

Maximum value:

Amplitude:

Period:

Frequency:

Assignment

Name _____ Date _____

Identical?
Trigonometric Identities

Match each expression with an equivalent expression.

1. $\sin x$ **a.** $\sec\left(\dfrac{\pi}{2} - x\right)$

2. $\cos x$ **b.** $\dfrac{1}{\cos x}$

3. $\tan x$ **c.** $\sin(x + 2\pi)$

4. $\csc x$ **d.** $\cos(-x)$

5. $\sec x$ **e.** $\dfrac{\cos x}{\sin x}$

6. $\cot x$ **f.** $\dfrac{\sin x}{\cos x}$

Confirm that the statement is true. Show all your work.

7. $\dfrac{\sin x}{\tan x} = \cos x$ **8.** $\sin^2 x(1 + \cot^2 x) = 1$

9. $\tan\theta\cos\theta + \sin(-\theta) = 0$ **10.** $\sin y = \cos y \cot\left(\dfrac{\pi}{2} - y\right)$

11. $\tan x \sec x = \dfrac{\sin x}{\cos^2 x}$

12. $\sec \theta = \dfrac{\csc \theta + \sec \theta}{\cot \theta + 1}$

13. $\tan x = \dfrac{\sec^2 x}{\cot x + \tan x}$

14. $\dfrac{\cos x \csc(x + 2\pi)}{\cot(x + \pi)} = 1$

15. $\tan^2 u = \dfrac{\sec u}{\cos(-u)} - 1$

16. $\sin y \sec y(\sec y \csc y + \tan y) = 1$

11

Assignment

Name _____ Date _____

Solutions
Solving Trigonometric Equations

Solve the equation over the given domain.

1. $\cos x = \dfrac{1}{2}$ over the domain $0 \le x \le 2\pi$

2. $\sin y = 0.875$ over the domain $-\dfrac{\pi}{2} \le y \le \dfrac{\pi}{2}$

3. $\tan u = \dfrac{1}{\sqrt{3}}$ over the domain of all real numbers

4. $3 \tan x - 5 = -2$ over the domain of all real numbers

5. $5 \cos z + 1 = 3$ over the domain $0 \le z \le \pi$

6. $8 \sin x - 4 = 3$ over the domain of all real numbers

7. $4 \cos^2 x = 1$ over the domain $0 \le x \le 2\pi$

8. $4 \sin^2 x + 17 \sin x + 4 = 0$ over the domain of all real numbers

9. $3 \tan^2 y = 2 - \tan y$ over the domain of all real numbers

10. $5 \cos^2 x = 2 \cos x$ over the domain of all real numbers

Assignment

Name _____ Date _____

Rabbits and Seasonal Affective Disorder
Applications of Circular Functions

Some people believe in the biorhythm theory. This theory states that a person's functioning is controlled by three factors: a physical cycle, an emotional cycle, and an intellectual cycle. Each factor can by modeled by a sine function. A value of 1 indicates a day for which a cycle is at a high point, a value of −1 indicates a day for which a cycle is at a low point, and a value of 0 indicates a day of vulnerability or risk. The physical cycle has a period of 23 days, the emotional cycle has a period of 28 days, and the intellectual cycle has a period of 33 days.

Use this information to answer Questions 1–6.

1. A person's physical cycle can be modeled by the function $p(x) = \sin\left(\dfrac{2\pi}{23}x\right)$, where x is the number of days since the person was born. Explain how you know that the period of this function is 23 days.

2. Write functions for the emotional cycle $m(x)$ and the intellectual cycle $n(x)$.

3. Calculate the number of days that you have been alive. Remember to consider leap years. Then use your age in days to evaluate each of the three functions to determine the factors for your current physical, emotional, and intellectual states. Round your answers to the nearest hundredth, if necessary.

4. What do the values in the previous question indicate about your physical, emotional, and intellectual states?

5. Graph the functions for your physical, emotional, and intellectual cycles for all of the days of the current month on the grid.

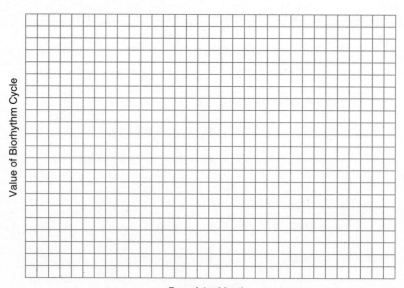

Day of the Month

6. Based on your graph, what would someone who believes in biorhythms think is your "best" day of the month? What would they think is the "worst" day? Explain your reasoning.

The average daily temperature for the city of Denver, Colorado, can be modeled by a sine function. The following tables show data for the average temperature in degrees Fahrenheit in Denver throughout the year.

Use this information to answer Questions 7–9.

Date	Day	Average Temperature
Dec. 31	0	29°
Jan. 10	10	29°
Jan. 20	20	29°
Jan. 30	30	30°
Feb. 9	40	32°
Feb. 19	50	34°
Mar. 1	60	36°
Mar. 11	70	38°
Mar. 21	80	41°
Mar. 31	90	43°
Apr. 10	100	46°
Apr. 20	110	49°
Apr. 30	120	52°
May 10	130	55°
May 20	140	59°
May 30	150	62°
June 9	160	66°
June 19	170	69°
June 29	180	71°

Date	Day	Average Temperature
July 9	190	73°
July 19	200	74°
July 29	210	74°
Aug. 8	220	73°
Aug. 18	230	72°
Aug. 28	240	69°
Sept. 7	250	65°
Sept. 17	260	62°
Sept. 27	270	58°
Oct. 7	280	55°
Oct. 17	290	51°
Oct. 27	300	46°
Nov. 6	310	41°
Nov. 16	320	37°
Nov. 26	330	34°
Dec. 6	340	32°
Dec. 16	350	30°
Dec. 26	360	29°

11

7. Plot the points from the table using the day of the year for the independent variable and the average daily temperature for the dependent variable.

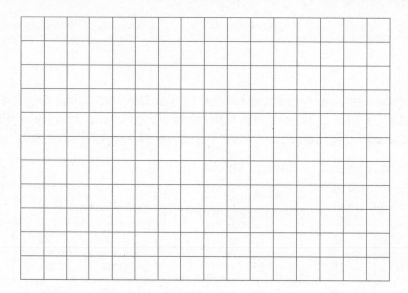

8. Write a sine function of the form $f(x) = A \sin(Bx + C) + D$ that models the data.

9. From the function of the form $f(x) = A \sin(Bx + C) + D$ that you wrote in Question 8, determine what each of the parameters represents in terms of the situation.

a. What does A represent?

b. What does B represent?

c. What does C represent?

d. What does *D* represent?

11

Assignment

Name _____ Date _____

Angle-Angle-Side and Angle-Side-Angle
Law of Sines

Use the law of sines to calculate the missing side length, *x*. Round your
answers to the nearest hundredth, if necessary.

1.

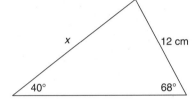

2.

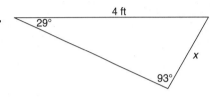

3.

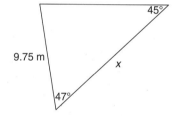

4.

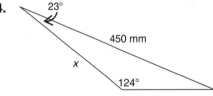

Use the law of sines to calculate the missing angle measure, θ. Round your
answers to the nearest hundredth, if necessary.

5.

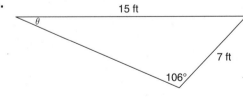

6.

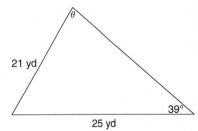

7.

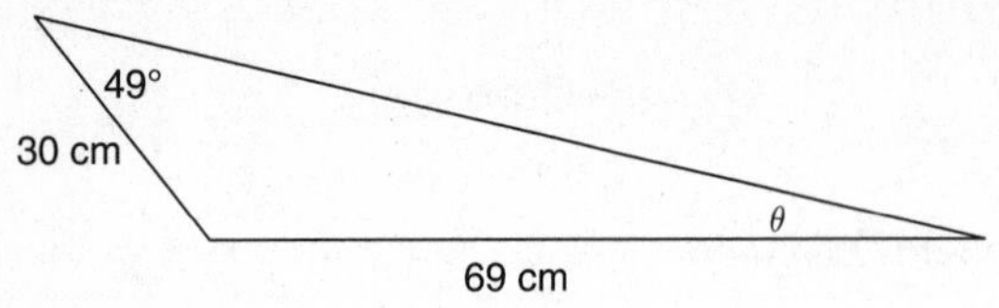

8.

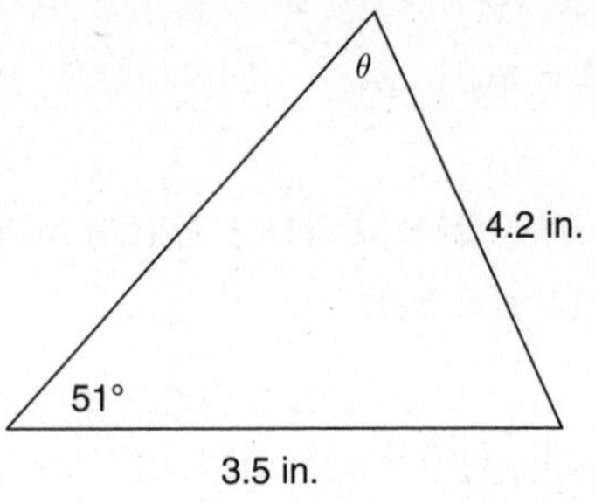

11

9. A disabled ship is sighted from two different lighthouses, as shown in the diagram. Calculate the distance from the ship to the nearest lighthouse. Round your answer to the nearest hundredth, if necessary.

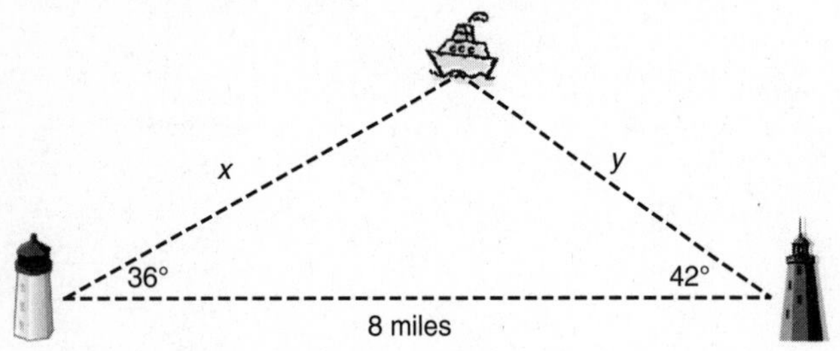

Assignment

Name _____ Date _____

Side-Angle-Side and Side-Side-Side
Law of Cosines

Use the law of cosines to calculate the missing angle measure, θ. Round
your answers to the nearest hundredth, if necessary.

1.

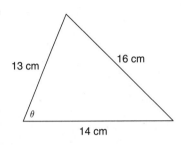

13 cm 16 cm θ 14 cm

2.

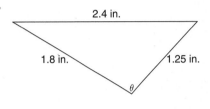

2.4 in. 1.8 in. 1.25 in. θ

3.

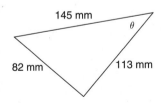

145 mm θ 82 mm 113 mm

4.

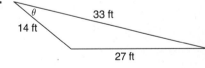

θ 33 ft 14 ft 27 ft

Use the law of cosines to calculate the missing side length, *x*. Round your answers to the nearest hundredth, if necessary.

5.

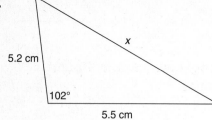

5.2 cm

x

102°

5.5 cm

6.

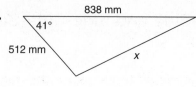

838 mm

41°

512 mm

x

7.

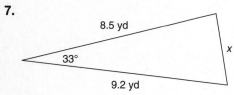

8.5 yd

x

33°

9.2 yd

8.

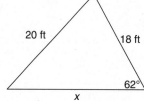

20 ft

18 ft

62°

x

9. Lifeguard stands are arranged on a beach as shown in the diagram. The stand at point *B* is 88 yards from the stand at point *A,* and the stand at point *C* is 80 yards from the stand at point *B*. The stands make an angle of 150° at vertex *B*. A buoy line runs in a straight line from point *A* to point *C* to mark a division between the shallow and deep waters. About how long is the buoy line? Round your answer to the nearest yard, if necessary.

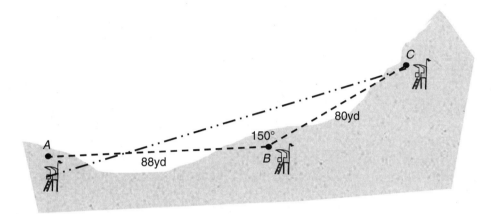

11

Assignment

Name _____ Date _____

College Tutoring
Introduction to Arithmetic Sequences

For each sequence, list the next three terms and describe how each new term was generated. Then determine if the sequence is an arithmetic sequence.

1. $-6, -1, 4, 9, 14, \ldots$

2. $30, 24, 18, 12, 6, \ldots$

3. $-1, 3, -9, 27, \ldots$

4. $1, 3, 7, 15, 31, \ldots$

Write the first six terms of the arithmetic sequence with the given criteria.

5. The first term of the sequence is 4 and the common difference is 10.

6. The first term of the sequence is 0 and the common difference is -2.5.

7. The first term of the sequence is -5 and the common difference is 6.

8. The first term of the sequence is -8 and the common difference is $-\dfrac{1}{2}$.

Write the first 6 terms of the arithmetic sequence with the given explicit formula. Identify the common difference *d*. Then write the recursive formula for the sequence.

9. $a_n = 2n - 7$

10. $a_n = -5n + 1$

11. $a_n = 3(n - 1) + 11$

12. $a_n = -6(n - 1) - 9$

Write an explicit and recursive formula that represents the *n*th term of the arithmetic sequence.

13. 1, 4, 7, 10, . . .

14. 6, 4, 2, 0, . . .

15. 9, 5, 1, −3, . . .

16. 1, $\frac{4}{3}$, $\frac{5}{3}$, 2, $\frac{7}{3}$, . . .

Assignment

Name _____ Date _____

Too Much Homework!
Introduction to Geometric Sequences

For each sequence, list the next three terms and describe how each new term was generated. Then determine if the sequence is a geometric sequence.

1. 5, 10, 15, 20, 25, . . .

2. 2, 6, 18, 54, . . .

3. 1, −2, 4, −8, 16, . . .

4. 80, 40, 20, 10, 5, . . .

Write the first six terms of the geometric sequence with the given criteria.

5. The first term of the sequence is −3 and the common ratio is 4.

6. The first term of the sequence is 1 and the common ratio is $\frac{1}{3}$.

7. The first term of the sequence is 8 and the common ratio is −10.

8. The first term of the sequence is −128 and the common ratio is −0.25.

Write the first 6 terms of the geometric sequence with the given explicit formula. Identify the common ratio r. Then write the recursive formula for the sequence.

9. $g_n = 3 \cdot 2^{n-1}$

10. $g_n = -6 \cdot 3^{n-1}$

11. $g_n = 256 \cdot \left(\dfrac{1}{2}\right)^{n-1}$

12. $g_n = 4 \cdot (-2)^{n-1}$

12

Write an explicit and recursive formula that represents the nth term of the arithmetic sequence.

13. $-7, -14, -28, -56, \ldots$

14. $2, -8, 32, -128, \ldots$

15. $5, 15, 45, 135, \ldots$

16. $-100, 150, -225, 337.5$

Assignment

Name _____ Date _____

Sums a Lot
Introduction to Linear Functions

Calculate the indicated sum of the series. Then determine whether the series is an arithmetic series or a geometric series. If the series is arithmetic, calculate the common difference *d*. If the series is geometric, calculate the common ratio *r*.

1. $20 + 17 + 14 + 11 + 8$; S_3

2. $1 + 3 + 9 + 27 + 81$; S_4

3. $16 + 8 + 4 + 2 + 1$; S_5

4. $20 + 28 + 36 + 44 + 52$; S_2

Write an explicit formula that you can use to compute the *n*th term of the arithmetic sequence. Then calculate the specified sum.

5. $3, 7, 11, 15, \ldots$; S_{25}

6. $21, 15, 9, 3, \ldots$; S_{30}

7. $-7, -5, -3, -1, \ldots$; S_{15}

8. $-37, -32, -27, -22, \ldots$; S_{18}

Calculate the specified sum of the geometric sequence.

9. $729, 243, 81, 27, \ldots; \; S_{10}$

10. $1, 2, 4, 8, \ldots; \; S_{18}$

11. $10, 5, \dfrac{5}{2}, \dfrac{5}{4}, \dfrac{5}{8}, \ldots; \; S_{11}$

12. $0.2, 0.8, 3.2, 12.8, \ldots; \; S_{12}$

12

13. Suppose your parents give you $3 allowance after the first week of the year. They agree to increase your allowance by $1 every week for the remainder of the year.

   a. What is the total allowance you will have received after the 10th week of the year?

   b. What is the total allowance you will have received after the 25th week of the year?

c. What is the total allowance you will have received for the year? (Note: There are 52 weeks in one year.)

14. You propose a new plan for your allowance for next year. You ask that your parents give you 1 penny after the first week of the year, and then triple your allowance every week for the remainder of the year.

a. Write a formula that you can use to calculate the total allowance (in dollars) you will have received after the nth week of the year under the new plan.

b. What is the total allowance you will have received after the 10th week of the year?

c. What is the total allowance you will have received after the 20th week of the year?

d. Do you think that your parents will agree with your proposal? Why or why not?

12

Assignment

Name _____ Date _____

Summing Forever
Sum of an Infinite Geometric Series

Draw a diagram to represent the infinite geometric series. Use the diagram to estimate the sum of the series.

1. $2 + 1 + \dfrac{1}{2} + \dfrac{1}{4} + \dfrac{1}{8} + \dfrac{1}{16} + \ldots$

2. $4 + 1 + \dfrac{1}{4} + \dfrac{1}{16} + \dfrac{1}{64} + \dfrac{1}{256} + \ldots$

Identify the common ratio r and the first term a_1 of the geometric series. Then determine if the series has a sum. If so, calculate the sum.

3. $\dfrac{5}{6} + \dfrac{5}{12} + \dfrac{5}{24} + \dfrac{5}{48} + \dfrac{5}{96} + \ldots$

4. $\dfrac{8}{27} + \dfrac{4}{9} + \dfrac{2}{3} + 1 + \dfrac{3}{2} + \ldots$

5. $\dfrac{2}{5} + \dfrac{2}{15} + \dfrac{2}{45} + \dfrac{2}{135} + \dfrac{2}{405} + \ldots$

6. $20 + 15 + \dfrac{45}{4} + \dfrac{135}{16} + \dfrac{405}{64} + \ldots$

7. $4 + 5 + \dfrac{25}{4} + \dfrac{125}{16} + \dfrac{625}{64} + \ldots$

8. $1 + 0.2 + 0.04 + 0.008 + 0.0016 + \ldots$

9. $12 + 10 + \dfrac{25}{3} + \dfrac{125}{18} + \dfrac{625}{108} + \ldots$

10. $\dfrac{3}{4} + \dfrac{1}{2} + \dfrac{1}{3} + \dfrac{2}{9} + \dfrac{4}{27} + \ldots$

11. $100 + 80 + 64 + 51.2 + 40.96 + \ldots$

12. $\dfrac{1}{40} + \dfrac{1}{20} + \dfrac{1}{10} + \dfrac{1}{5} + \dfrac{2}{5} + \ldots$

Assignment

Name _____ Date _____

Rolling, Flipping, and Pulling
Probability and Sample Spaces

List all of the possible outcomes to show the sample space for the event. Then determine the probability of the event.

1. rolling a 3 on a six-sided number cube

2. flipping a coin three times and getting tails all three times

3. choosing a red tile from a bag of 4 red tiles and 6 blue tiles

4. drawing a number less than 8 from a stack of nine cards numbered 2 through 10

5. flipping a coin twice and getting at least one tail

6. choosing a blue tile from a bag of 3 yellow tiles, 4 red tiles, and 5 green tiles

7. drawing the number 6 from a standard deck of playing cards

8. rolling two number cubes and getting a sum that is an even number

Suppose that you roll a six-sided number cube and then you spin the spinner shown.

9. Make a table to show the sample space of the events.

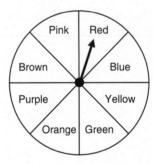

10. What are the total number of possible outcomes?

11. Are the events dependent or independent?

12. Use your table to determine the probability of rolling a 1 and the spinner landing on green.

13. Use your table to determine the probability of rolling an odd number and the spinner landing on red.

14. Use your table to determine the probability of rolling a number greater than 2 and the spinner landing on a color that begins with the letter B.

15. Use your table to determine the probability of rolling a number less than 7 and the spinner landing on yellow.

16. Use your table to determine the probability of rolling an even number and the spinner landing on gray.

13

13

© 2008 Carnegie Learning, Inc.

Assignment

Name _____ Date _____

Multiple Trials
Compound Probability

A local deli offers three types of bread—white, rye, and wheat; five types of meat—ham, turkey, pastrami, chicken, and roast beef; and four types of cheese—American, Swiss, provolone, and cheddar. Their lunch special includes a sandwich on your choice of bread with one type of meat and one type of cheese for $3.25.

Determine the probability that a random customer orders the given type of sandwich during the lunch special. Assume that each sandwich includes bread, meat, and cheese.

1. a pastrami sandwich

2. a sandwich with provolone cheese

3. a sandwich not on wheat bread

4. a turkey sandwich on rye bread

5. a ham or chicken sandwich

6. a sandwich that is not turkey and not on white bread

7. a roast beef sandwich with American cheese

8. a sandwich that is on white bread with cheddar cheese

9. a ham sandwich with cheddar cheese on wheat bread

10. a pastrami sandwich with Swiss cheese on white bread

Suppose you are playing a game in which you spin two spinners. If the sum of the numbers on the spinners is an odd number, you win a prize. Use this information and the diagram of the spinners shown to answer Questions 11–15.

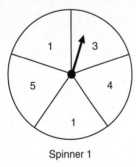

Spinner 1

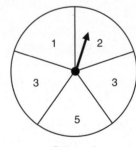

Spinner 2

11. What is the probability of spinning an even number on the first spinner and an even number on the second spinner? Would you win a prize? Explain.

12. What is the probability of spinning an even number on the first spinner and an odd number on the second spinner? Would you win a prize? Explain.

13. What is the probability of spinning an odd number on the first spinner and an even number on the second spinner? Would you win a prize? Explain.

14. What is the probability of spinning an odd number on the first spinner and an odd number on the second spinner? Would you win a prize? Explain.

15. What is the probability of winning the game?

16. Do you think that the game is fair? Why or why not?

Assignment

Name _____ Date _____

Counting
Permutations and Combinations

Calculate the factorial.

1. $6!$

2. $11!$

3. $\dfrac{5!}{2!}$

4. $\dfrac{9!3!}{6!4!}$

Calculate the permutation.

5. $_5P_2$

6. $_7P_1$

7. $_4P_4$

8. $_8P_7$

Calculate the combination.

9. $_6C_4$

10. $_5C_1$

11. $_8C_8$

12. $_7C_6$

13

Six friends decide to go to the movie theater: Tisha, Alberto, Rosa, Carlos, Lucy, and Brian. The friends want to sit next to each other in the same row. Use this information to answer Questions 13–15.

13. Suppose that the order the friends sit is not important.

   a. In how many different ways can they be seated?

   b. In how many different ways can Tisha sit next to Rosa?

   c. What is the probability that Tisha sits next to Rosa?

14. Suppose that the friends sit so that all of the boys are grouped together and all of the girls are grouped together.

   a. In how many different ways can they be seated?

   Boys on left, girls on right:

   Girls on left, boys on right:

   b. In how many different ways can Alberto sit next to Brian?

c. What is the probability that Alberto sits next to Brian?

15. Suppose that the movie is about to sell out and there are only 4 tickets left. The friends decide that 4 of them will see the movie and the other 2 will see it another time.

a. If they randomly choose the group that will see the movie, how many possible groups are there?

b. What is the probability that Tisha, Alberto, Rosa, and Carlos will be seeing the movie together?

13

Assignment

Name _____ Date _____

Pascal and Independent Events
Pascal's Triangle and the Binomial Theorem

Make a sketch of the values of the first 10 rows of Pascal's Triangle. Then use your sketch to answer Questions 1–4.

1. What is the probability of getting 1 head and 3 tails if a coin is flipped four times?

2. What is the probability of getting 5 heads and 1 tail if a coin is flipped six times?

3. What is the probability of getting 3 heads and 4 tails if a coin is flipped seven times?

4. What is the probability of getting 2 heads and 6 tails if a coin is flipped eight times?

Use the Binomial Theorem to calculate the term.

5. sixth term of $(x + y)^9$

6. third term of $(x - 2y)^{16}$

7. fourth term of $(x - y)^{21}$

8. 99th term of $(3x + y)^{100}$

Use the binomial distribution to calculate the probability.

9. Determine the probability of getting 10 heads and 8 tails when flipping a coin 18 times.

10. Determine the probability of getting 6 heads and 8 tails when flipping a coin 14 times.

11. Determine the probability of getting exactly 5 ones when rolling a number cube 15 times.

12. Determine the probability of getting exactly 2 threes when rolling a number cube 13 times.

13. Determine the probability of getting exactly 2 spins landing on green when spinning the spinner at the right 10 times.

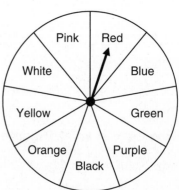

14. Determine the probability of getting exactly 3 spins landing on red when spinning the spinner at the right 9 times.

Assignment

Name _____ Date _____

The Theoretical and the Actual
Experimental Versus Theoretical Probability

Determine whether the statement is based on theoretical or experimental probability. Explain your answer.

1. The probability that a person chooses vanilla as his or her favorite type of ice cream is $\frac{1}{6}$.

2. The probability that you will choose a king from a standard deck of shuffled cards is $\frac{1}{13}$.

3. The probability that you get 2 tails when you flip a coin 5 times is $\frac{5}{16}$.

4. The probability that a person chosen at random is left-handed is $\frac{1}{10}$.

13

Suppose you roll a six-sided number cube 30 times. Your results are shown in the table. Use the table to answer Questions 5–8.

Outcome	1	2	3	4	5	6
Result	10	4	5	2	9	0

5. What is the experimental probability that you roll a 3 on your next roll? What is the theoretical probability that you roll a 3 on your next roll?

6. What is the experimental probability that you roll an even number on your next roll? What is the theoretical probability that you roll an even number on your next roll?

7. What is the experimental probability that you roll a number less than 6 on your next roll? What is the theoretical probability that you roll a number less than 6 on your next roll?

8. What is the experimental probability that you roll a 1 and then roll another 1 on your next two rolls? What is the theoretical probability that you roll a 1 and then roll another 1 on your next two rolls?

Name_____ Date _____

Suppose you recorded the number of days it rained and determined that during the past 50 days, it rained on 12 of those days. Use this information to answer Questions 9–12. Write your answers as percents.

9. Based on your experiment, what is the probability that it will rain tomorrow?

10. Based on your experiment, what is the probability that it will rain the next two days in a row?

11. Based on your experiment, what is the probability that it will rain tomorrow or rain the next day?

12. Based on your experiment, what is the probability that it will rain the next three days in a row?

13

13

© 2008 Carnegie Learning, Inc.

Assignment

Name _____ Date _____

Averages
Measures of Central Tendency, Quartiles, and Percentiles

Calculate the mean, median, mode, range, and quartiles of the data set. Then draw a box-and-whisker plot for the data set.

1. 10, 9, 9, 2, 11, 15, 4, 9, 12, 16, 8, 7, 5

2. 25, 32, 16, 40, 25, 33, 39, 40, 19, 22, 40, 35, 25, 32, 21, 33

14

3. 516, 422, 301, 695, 472, 486, 478, 575, 603, 411

4. 4.3, 0.8, 1.5, 3.4, 2.1, 3.0, 0.9, 3.4, 3.2, 1.1, 1.8, 2.9, 2.1, 3.4, 4.6

Name_____ Date _____

You are participating in a bowling tournament for charity. The bowling scores after the first game for the 25 people participating in the event are shown.

140, 96, 115, 162, 80, 175, 201, 128, 129, 265, 111, 152, 141, 138, 133, 155, 149, 142, 96, 108, 120, 122, 153, 147, 112

Use this data for Questions 5–11.

   5. Arrange the data from the lowest score to the highest score.

   6. Calculate the mean, median, mode, range, and quartiles of the data set.

   7. Draw a box-and-whisker plot for the data set.

   8. Which score(s) are above the 75th percentile?

   9. Which score(s) are below the 25th percentile?

10. Suppose your bowling score was 175. At what percentile is your score?

11. Describe how your score compares to the other participants' scores.

14

Assignment

Name _____ Date _____

Spread
Variation and Standard Deviation

Complete the table to calculate the variance and standard deviation of the data set.

1.

x_i	$x_i - \overline{X}$	$\left(x_i - \overline{X}\right)^2$
26		
75		
88		
95		
107		
112		
183		

14

2.

x_i	$x_i - \overline{X}$	$\left(x_i - \overline{X}\right)^2$
0.72		
0.8		
0.95		
0.99		
1.1		
1.2		

Use a calculator to calculate the mean, median, variance, and standard deviation of the data set.

3. 12, 15, 12, 11, 14, 16, 15, 12, 11, 10, 14, 13

4. 52, 36, 88, 12, 44, 65, 21, 105, 98, 39

5. 0.36, 0.4, 0.52, 0.61, 0.33, 0.47, 0.6, 0.44, 0.59, 0.53, 0.38, 0.45, 0.58, 0.46, 0.51

6. 546, 123, 307, 555, 469, 117, 299, 626, 518, 460, 504, 190, 287

The data shows the length of time that travelers had to wait in the security checkpoint lines of two airports during the same time on the same day. Use this data for Questions 7–10.

Airport A: 5, 7, 13, 12, 10, 12, 9, 22, 7, 7, 10, 9, 18, 2, 5

Airport B: 2, 19, 1, 4, 21, 18, 1, 3, 17, 20, 2, 5, 8, 4, 20

7. Calculate the mean and range of the waiting times for both airports.

8. Can you draw any conclusions from the mean and range about how the wait times compare? Why or why not?

14

9. Complete the tables and use them to calculate the variance and standard deviation of the data sets.

Airport A			Airport B		
x_i	$\lvert x_i - \overline{X} \rvert$	$\left(x_i - \overline{X}\right)^2$	x_i	$\lvert x_i - \overline{X} \rvert$	$\left(x_i - \overline{X}\right)^2$

10. If you want the shortest possible wait and can choose either airport, which one would you choose? Explain your answer.

Assignment

Name _____ Date _____

Normal?
Distribution

A set of data is normally distributed with a mean of 0 and a standard deviation of 1. Use your graphing calculator to calculate the probability. Round your answer to the nearest ten thousandth, if necessary.

1. $P(-2 < x < 2)$

2. $P(-3 < x < 0)$

3. $P(0 < x < 5)$

4. $P(-4 < x <)$

5. $P(-1 < x < 1)$

6. $P(-\infty < x < -2.5)$

The shoe sizes of the females in a high school are normally distributed with a mean of 8 and a standard deviation of 1. Use this information to answer Questions 7–10.

7. Use the normalcdf(lowerbound, upperbound,) function on a graphing calculator to graph the distribution of the shoe sizes of the females in the school. Sketch a graph of the function in the grid.

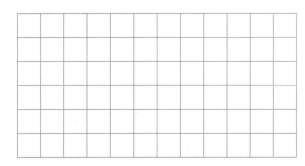

8. What is the probability that the shoe size of a female student chosen at random is smaller than 8? Write your answer as a percent.

9. What is the probability that the shoe size of a female student chosen at random is between 9.5 and 11? Write your answer as a percent.

14

10. What is the probability that the shoe size of a female student chosen at random is larger than 6? Write your answer as a percent.

The lengths of the adult northern pike in a lake are normally distributed with a mean of 23 inches and a standard deviation of 4.3 inches. Use this information to answer Questions 11–14.

11. Use the normalcdf(lowerbound, upperbound, μ, σ) function on a graphing calculator to graph the distribution of the lengths of northern pike in the lake. Sketch a graph of the function in the grid.

12. What is the probability that you catch a northern pike that is less than 1 foot long? Write your answer as a percent.

13. What is the probability that you catch a northern pike that is between 2 and 3 feet long? Write your answer as a percent.

14. What is the probability that you catch a northern pike that is more than $1\frac{1}{2}$ feet long? Write your answer as a percent.

14

Assignment

Name _____ Date _____

Line of Best Fit
Linear Regressions

Use your graphing calculator to determine the linear regression line for the data set. Then determine the correlation coefficient and interpret the quality of the fit of the line. Round all decimals to the nearest hundredth.

1. $(5, 6)$, $(-3, -4)$, $(10, 13)$, $(8, 7)$, $(0, -1)$, $(-4, -3)$

2. $(0.3, 0.2)$, $(0.1, 0.1)$, $(0, -0.1)$, $(0.2, 0.3)$, $(-0.1, 0.2)$, $(0.5, 0)$, $(0.3, -0.1)$

3. $(-5, -2)$, $(0, 4)$, $(2, 3)$, $(4, 2)$, $(-2, 0)$, $(1, -1)$, $(-3, 3)$, $(-3, -2)$, $(5, 1)$

4. $(1, -32)$, $(8, -86)$, $(5, -41)$, $(2, -27)$, $(7, -69)$, $(3, -30)$, $(4, -48)$, $(0, -19)$, $(6, -29)$, $(8, -42)$

14

You are conducting a study to determine if the amount of sleep a mammal gets affects its life span. You collect data and record the average amount of sleep per night and the average maximum life span for 14 different mammals. Your results are shown in the table. Use this information to answer Questions 5–12.

Mammal	Maximum Life span (yrs)	Sleep (hrs per day)	Mammal	Maximum Life span (yrs)	Sleep (hrs per day)
Armadillo	18.1	7	Pig	27	8.4
Cow	30	3.9	Possum	19.4	5
Gray seal	41	6.2	Raccoon	13.7	12.5
Guinea pig	7.6	8.2	Rat	4.7	13.2
Horse	46	2.9	Red fox	9.8	9.8
Jaguar	22.4	10.8	Squirrel	9	13.8
Mouse	3.2	13.2	Wolf	16.2	13

5. Use your graphing calculator to determine the linear regression line for the maximum life span versus the number of hours of sleep per day.

6. Identify the slope and y-intercept of the line.

7. Would you say that the regression line is a good model for the data? Why or why not?

14

8. Plot the points from the table and graph the regression line in the grid.

9. What can you conclude about the amount of sleep a mammal gets and how the amount of sleep relates to the mammal's average maximum life span?

10. The average maximum life span of a hamster is about 4 years. Using the model, about how many hours of sleep per day would you estimate a hamster gets?

11. A donkey sleeps about 3.1 hours per day. Using the model, what would you estimate is the average maximum life span of a donkey?

12. Do you think that humans fit this model? Why or why not?

14

14

Assignment

Name _____ Date _____

Not All Data Are Linear
Other Regressions

Use your graphing calculator to determine the linear, quadratic, and exponential regression equations for the data set. Then graph the data points and the equations with the given window on your calculator and explain which equation(s) best fit the data.

1. (0.5, 2), (0, 1), (1.5, 1.5), (1, 0.5), (2, 2), (0.5, 0.5), (2, 2.5), (−1, 3.5)
   Window: $-2 \leq x \leq 4, 0 \leq y \leq 4$

2. (31, 22), (−10, 41), (−35, 89), (54, 15), (22, 20), (41, 18), (0, 28)
   Window: $-40 \leq x \leq 60, 0 \leq y \leq 100$

3. (1, 7), (4, 2), (6, 10), (2, 3), (5, 5), (0, 18), (3, 1), (7, 24), (5, 6)
   Window: $0 \leq x \leq 8, 0 \leq y \leq 30$

14

4. (−4, 5), (10, 2), (4, 3), (12, 1), (0, 4), (−6, 6)
  Window: −8 ≤ x ≤ 14, 0 ≤ y ≤ 10

The data in the table shows the number of post offices in the United States at the beginning of each decade from 1900 to 2000. Use this information to answer Questions 5–9.

Year	Number of Post Offices
1900	76,688
1910	59,580
1920	52,641
1930	49,063
1940	44,024
1950	41,464
1960	35,238
1970	32,002
1980	30,326
1990	28,959
2000	27,876

14

5. Sketch a scatter plot of the data in the grid. Let $x = 0$ represent the year 1900, $x = 10$ represent the year 1910, and so on.

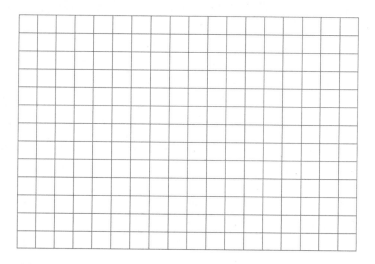

6. Use your graphing calculator to determine the linear, quadratic, and exponential regression equations for the data set.

7. Which regression equation best models the data? Graph this equation in the grid in Question 5.

8. Use the regression equation you chose in Question 7 to predict the number of post offices in the United States in the year 2050.

14

9. Use the regression equation you chose in Question 7 to predict when the number of post offices in the United States will reach 10,000.

14

Assignment

Name _____ Date _____

Arrays! Arrays!
Introduction to Matrices and Matrix Operations

Use the following matrices to perform the indicated operations.

$$V = \begin{bmatrix} 1 & -3 \\ -1 & -2 \\ 2 & 3 \end{bmatrix} \quad W = \begin{bmatrix} 2 & -4 & 5 \\ 8 & 6 & -1 \\ 0 & 3 & 8 \end{bmatrix} \quad X = \begin{bmatrix} 6 & -10 & 0 \\ -4 & 8 & -2 \end{bmatrix} \quad Y = \begin{bmatrix} 0 & -4 & -2 \\ -5 & -11 & 14 \\ 1 & 0 & -6 \end{bmatrix} \quad Z = \begin{bmatrix} -4 & 15 \\ 16 & -20 \\ -5 & 9 \end{bmatrix}$$

1. $V + Z$

2. $W - Y$

3. $X + X$

4. $10Y$

5. $2Z + 3V$

6. $\frac{1}{2}(Y - W)$

15

A small candle-making company sells candles of different scents and sizes. The available sizes are small, medium, and large. The available scents are vanilla (V), pine (P), apple (A), lavender (L), and berry (B). The matrix represents the number of candles the company sold last month. Use this information to answer Questions 7–13.

$$
\begin{array}{c c}
& \begin{array}{ccccc} \text{V} & \text{P} & \text{A} & \text{L} & \text{B} \end{array} \\
\begin{array}{c} \text{Small:} \\ \text{Medium:} \\ \text{Large:} \end{array} &
\begin{bmatrix} 12 & 2 & 9 & 6 & 15 \\ 17 & 3 & 13 & 7 & 11 \\ 14 & 1 & 8 & 7 & 10 \end{bmatrix}
\end{array}
$$

7. What are the dimensions of the matrix?

8. What does the entry a_{32} represent?

9. How many small berry-scented candles did the company sell last month?

10. What size candle was the most popular last month? How do you know?

11. What scent of candle was the least popular last month? How do you know?

12. How many total candles did the company sell last month? Explain how you calculated your answer.

15

13. The matrix shown represents the number of candles that the company has sold so far this month. Suppose that the company set a goal this month to sell twice as many of each size and scent of candle as they did last month. Write a matrix to show how many more candles the company needs to sell this month to reach their goal.

$$
\begin{array}{c}
\\
\text{Small:} \\
\text{Medium:} \\
\text{Large:}
\end{array}
\begin{array}{ccccc}
\text{V} & \text{P} & \text{A} & \text{L} & \text{B} \\
\left[\begin{array}{ccccc}
22 & 4 & 13 & 10 & 15 \\
30 & 6 & 24 & 13 & 22 \\
28 & 1 & 9 & 11 & 15
\end{array}\right]
\end{array}
$$

15

15

Assignment

Name _____ Date _____

Rows times Columns
Matrix Multiplication

Use the following matrices to perform the indicated operations, if possible. If it is not possible, explain why.

$$K = \begin{bmatrix} 0 & -3 \\ -1 & 5 \end{bmatrix} \qquad L = \begin{bmatrix} 6 & -4 & 3 \\ -1 & 1 & -2 \end{bmatrix} \qquad M = \begin{bmatrix} -3 & -3 \\ -7 & 1 \\ 0 & 8 \end{bmatrix} \qquad N = \begin{bmatrix} 2 & 4 & -1 \\ -5 & 1 & 10 \\ 1 & 0 & -3 \end{bmatrix}$$

1. KL

2. LK

3. K^2

4. ML

5. L^2

6. NM

15

7. NL

8. MKL

9. K^3

10. N^2M

15

Assignment

Name _____ Date _____

Solving Systems of Linear Equations
Matrices

Solve the system of equations using Gaussian elimination. Show all of your work and describe each step.

1. $\begin{cases} 2x - 6y = 18 \\ x + 5y = -15 \end{cases}$

2. $\begin{cases} 3x + 2y = 4 \\ -5x - 6y = -4 \end{cases}$

3. $\begin{cases} -x + y = 3 \\ 4x - 7y = -6 \end{cases}$

4. $\begin{cases} 10x + 25y = -15 \\ 15x + 40y = -20 \end{cases}$

5. $\begin{cases} 5x + 10y = 15 \\ -3x - 4y = -16 \end{cases}$

15

6. $\begin{cases} 15x - 9y = 255 \\ -8x + 6y = 80 \end{cases}$

15

7. $\begin{cases} 2x + 3y - z = 4 \\ x - 2y + z = -1 \\ -x + y - 4z = 7 \end{cases}$

15

8. $\begin{cases} 2x + 4y - 2z = 1 \\ 2x + y + z = 10 \\ 4x + 2y - 2z = -4 \end{cases}$

15

15

Assignment

Name _____ Date _____

Multiplicative Inverses
Solving Matrix Equations

Calculate the multiplicative inverse of the matrix. Show all of your work and describe each step. Then check your answer.

1. $A = \begin{bmatrix} 5 & 4 \\ 3 & 2 \end{bmatrix}$

2. $B = \begin{bmatrix} 0 & 2 \\ -1 & -6 \end{bmatrix}$

3. $C = \begin{bmatrix} 5 & 3 \\ 1.5 & 1 \end{bmatrix}$

4. $D = \begin{bmatrix} -8 & 10 \\ -3 & 4 \end{bmatrix}$

15

Name_____ Date _____

Use a calculator to determine the inverse of the matrix, and use the inverse to solve the system of equations. Then check your solutions.

5. $\begin{cases} 3x - 5y = 7 \\ -x + 2y = -1 \end{cases}$

6. $\begin{cases} -5x - 4y = -14 \\ 3x + y = -7 \end{cases}$

7. $\begin{cases} -2x + 5y = -6 \\ x - 8y = 3 \end{cases}$

8. $\begin{cases} 10x + 4y = -9 \\ -5x + 3y = 4 \end{cases}$

© 2008 Carnegie Learning, Inc.

15

15

Assignment

Name _____ Date _____

Calories and Lunch
Applications of Matrices

You work in a dry cleaning shop. The shop cleans shirts, pants, and suits, and charges a different price to clean each type of item. Your manager has asked you to keep track of the customers' orders and the numbers of shirts, pants, and suits being cleaned. The table shows the last three customers' orders and the total cost of each order.

	Shirts	Pants	Suits	Total Cost
Customer A	6	2	1	$32
Customer B	10	4	2	$60
Customer C	5	4	0	$32

1. Define a matrix that shows all of the information in the table.

   a. What are the dimensions of the matrix?

   b. In the matrix, what does the entry in the second row and third column represent?

   c. In the matrix, what does the entry in the third row and fourth column represent?

15

2. Let x represent the cost of cleaning a shirt, let y represent the cost of cleaning a pair of pants, and let z represent the cost of cleaning a suit.

a. Use the information in the table to calculate matrices D and E for the matrix equation shown.

$$D \begin{bmatrix} x \\ y \\ z \end{bmatrix} = E$$

b. Calculate the values of x, y, and z by solving the matrix equation. Interpret these values in the context of the problem.

You are in charge of making gift bags to give away as prizes in raffles at a charity event. You are making gift bags for the first-, second-, and third-place winners of each raffle. The table shows the quantity of each type of item in each gift bag and the total amount each bag is worth based on the cost of the items.

	Season Tickets to Local Professional Baseball Games	Movie Passes	Music CDs	Amount Gift Bag is Worth
First Prize	4	20	5	$1235
Second Prize	2	12	4	$656
Third Prize	2	5	2	$570

3. Define a matrix that shows all of the information in the table.

© 2008 Carnegie Learning, Inc.

15

4. Suppose there are four raffles being held during the course of the charity event, so you need to make gift bags for the prizes for all four raffles.

a. How many total season tickets will you need?

b. How many total movie passes will you need?

c. How many total CDs will you need?

5. Let x represent the amount each season ticket is worth, let y represent the amount each movie pass is worth, and let z represent the amount each CD is worth.

a. Use the information in the table to calculate matrices D and E for the matrix equation shown.

$$D \begin{bmatrix} x \\ y \\ z \end{bmatrix} = E$$

b. Calculate the values of x, y, and z by solving the matrix equation. Interpret these values in the context of the problem.

15